LEYTON ORIENT

ORIENT

THE OFFICIAL
QUIZ
BOOK
1881-2012

NEILSON N. KAUFMAN

Dedication

This book is dedicated to my mother Millie Kaufman and my father Zalic 'Sid' Kaufman, who first planted the seed about the O's. He would tell me about the great O's players he watched back in the twenties up to the early fifties and, in 1957 taking me to Brisbane Road for the first time to watch such great players as Tommy Johnston, Phil Woosnam and later Eddy Brown, all of whom became personal friends, sadly only Phil is with us today.

The stories about the O's from my father, led me to want to find out more about the history of our grand club as I could find very little written on the subject (there was no internet or email in those days).

I first visited the Colindale Library in Brent and the local libraries in Hackney, some visits with my friend Alan Ravenhill, over many Saturday mornings to research the history of the O's and its early players, from its early days as a cricket team back in 1881, to turning professional and playing in the local leagues before entering the Southern League in 1904 and a year later being elected into the Football League.

It's at the Colindale Library that I first came across the names of Fred Parker, Billy Bower, Richard McFadden and all the early stars for the very first time and then researching about each one, so thanks Dad for planting that O's seed many years ago.

Also to my brother Alan Kaufman, who sadly succumbed to cancer back in October 2005. I remember watching with him the boys in royal blue and cheering them on to the top tier of English football and like many youngsters running on to the Brisbane Road pitch to lift skipper Stan Charlton into the air in celebration, and together watching us beat Chelsea in the FA Cup, both in 1972 and 1978, and to be honest quite a number of unexciting games, still that's what supporting the O's is all about, we just enjoyed being together watching the O's.

What of the future? Well, I have plans of starting my own dedicated history website on the O's and all its players and officials over the years. I have a database of over 3,500 players and officials, even down to the youth and trialist players with profiles on each, well, that's something for the future.

Finally, to all my O's friends, both fans, former players and officials, this O's quiz book is dedicated to you all, and as always…

Up Up the O's.

Neilson N. Kaufman
Johannesburg, South Africa
September 2012

LEYTON ORIENT

THE OFFICIAL

QUIZ BOOK

1881–2012

NEILSON N. KAUFMAN

PUBLISHING

Ordinarily I would have loved to have done a foreword for your new Orient Quiz book, but having just recently had an operation on my ankle, work in the law practice is now piling up and I'm afraid leaving me very little spare time for the more enjoyable things of life.

So, for now, I have two knee and now one ankle op which have resolved the accumulated damage of my very enjoyable footballing career of 13 years with the O's.

Please let me know how the quiz book goes and continue to keep in touch Up the O's.

Former Orient favourite Matthew Lockwood (left) pictured with Peter Allen.

Peter Allen

First published in Great Britain in 2012 by The Derby Books Publishing Company Limited, 3 The Parker Centre, Derby, DE21 4SZ.

ISBN 978-1-78091-067-3

Printed and bound by Gomer Press, Llandysul, Ceredigion.

Contents

Foreword

By Terry Mancini

After two years enjoying football in Port Elizabeth, South Africa, getting fitter and improving my concentration, I eventually won the SA League title with my teammates at PE City. I decided to return to the UK and try for another chance of making the grade in the English Football League.

An older experienced teammate at Watford (Cliff Holton) where I had started, had always kept in touch and said if I came back to the UK to let him know and he would get me a trial at whichever club he was still playing for. He was at Leyton Orient and there began my love affair with the O's, the ground and the fans.

At the time the club was going through a financial blip and only kept alive by the generosity of the directors with Harry Zussman (chairman) who owned a shoe factory in Shoreditch, paying most of the wages. In fact at most home games some of the supporters went around the ground at half-time with a blanket that supporters on the terraces threw coins in to help pay the bills.

I had my trial and all they could offer me was a month's contract but I had a feeling that things would work for me and the warmth and support from the team and the supporters would get us through difficult times.

In just three years and a new manager (Jimmy Bloomfield) I had captained the club to the Third Division Championship, which is still the last time the O's won a League championship.

I still look at their results every week wherever I am in the world and wait for another O's captain to lift a title Championship Cup for those very loyal and patient supporters.

I have to say we had some super players in that team and we had a great team spirit, essential for clubs with small budgets and small crowds. The friendliness of the players and supporters was something that I remember to this day and is essential for clubs the size of the O's.

Although I went on to play for QPR and gain promotion to the First Division with them and then onto Arsenal with their huge fan base and fabulous ground, the friendliness and support I remember at the O's was still something I never experienced at any other club.

One of those supporters, Neilson Kaufman, a lad from Hoxton, who became an Orient supporter following in his father and brothers' footsteps. He became a friend during those years and we have stayed in touch for more than 40 years.

He has written several books on Leyton Orient, Orient and the O's over the years and when he contacted me to ask if I would write a Foreword for this new quiz book 1881–2012, I was honoured and overwhelmed that he would ask.

Some footballers achieve greatness and are remembered by supporters by the way they played, the trophies they won, some by the number of goals they scored and some by the number of games they played for certain clubs.

I can't honestly claim any of those titles but I do know that being asked to write this Foreword is an honour that money, or fame can't buy. I do it for all those ex-Orient players I played with during my four years at Brisbane Road and for all the fantastic supporters who turned up week in and week out at a less fashionable football club in the East End to watch their team!

Thank you for your support and friendliness you gave to all of us during some difficult years and here's hoping the O's finally get another Championship and you can replace the sepia tinted photographs of me holding the Cup in the entrance hall at Leyton Orient.

Terry Mancini
Mancini Events
Mobile: 07770 653475
www.mancinievents.co.uk

Skipper Terry Mancini about to collect the Third Division Championship shield on 27 April 1970 from Mr Glikstein. On the left of Terry, in glasses, is a very happy chairman Harry Zussman. (Reproduced with the kind permission of David Bloomfield.)

Foreword

By Peter Kitchen

In 2006, I was among a number of former players and celebrities, who celebrated the 125th anniversary of the club's formation, with chairman Barry Hearn, then manager Martyn Ling and other staff at the club, and it was quite a surprise to learn just how long the O's have been around. This wonderful, old football club, may not have the glamour, support or resources of many of the other London clubs, but it is certainly a club with a big heart, a loyal fan base and an amazing and eventful history.

O's were the first English Football League club to enlist en masse into the army ranks heading off to fight in World War One, a feat honoured and celebrated last year with the unveiling of a memorial on the battlefields of the Somme in Northern France.

Over the years, there have been some wonderful and memorable times for the club and some great players and personalities have worn an Orient shirt, whether it was the white shirt with the red v, or the red braces kit that we wore in my time at the O's.

There have been occasions when the club has suffered hard financial times when the future of the club has been in doubt, but throughout its long history, the enduring qualities of the club, the fans and the people associated with it have always rallied to the cause to ensure its continued survival.

Orient supporters of the present and of the future will thoroughly enjoy reading and utilising this knowledgeable, informative and insightful new quiz book by Neil Kaufman as there will certainly be some amazing and obscure facts and statistics to test their Orient FC knowledge. Whether it's from the time when they were standing on the terraces behind the goals, in the old Brisbane Road Stand or as now cheering on their team in the relative luxury of the new West Stand, this book is a must for die hard O's fans and anyone connected with Leyton Orient FC.

I have personally known Neil Kaufman since 1977 and I can say with confidence, that no one is better qualified or equipped than Neil to write a quiz book about Leyton Orient FC. He has been the official club historian since 1972 and in more recent years he became the honorary historian of the club.

Neil is a lifelong O's supporter, first attending matches with his father and late brother in 1957, watching the O's in their one and only promotion to the top tier of English football and also following the O's during their wonderful FA Cup runs in the 1970s.

Neil has also written nine other books about the club and about various players including one about myself, *The Goal Gourmet, The Peter Kitchen Story*, which

Peter Kitchen is in the front row, second from left.

chronicles my own career as a professional footballer and the wonderful times I enjoyed, playing for this great little club and I am very proud to say that I have played a small part in writing some of that history and indirectly providing answers to some of the questions.

I hope you will enjoy reading this excellent book.

Peter Kitchen
July 2012

Foreword

By Brian Blower

I was very honoured to be asked to write a foreword to Neilson Kaufman's new book: *The Leyton Orient Official Quiz Book 1881–2012*.

Having known Neil since the late 1960s both as a great Orient supporter and a writer, he was always a person that could put me right with detailed history of his beloved Leyton Orient, facts and figures were always correct that he gave. I'm so pleased that I asked Neil to write a column in O's programmes back in 1973 on the O's history and a year later came his first ever book written on the club, along with Alan Ravenhill and nine books later we have this quiz book.

So when he asked me to do this foreword my answer was, 'Thank you very much YES it will be a great pleasure to assist with my contribution to what I know will be a fine publication.'

This quiz book is the first official quiz book on Leyton Orient and will be Neil's 10th book on the club and its players since 1974. All the research and questions are compiled by Neil, who started going down to Brisbane Road 1957, I've had a sneak preview of some of the questions and they are just great.

I'm sure this quiz book will be extremely welcomed by supporters of all ages; it will be well used in so many ways by all supporters, young and old. Supporters studying it and saying 'Do you remember' – in 1881 what sport did the club play before turning to football? 'What about this one' – name the O's prolific goalscorer between 1897 and 1902, and 'another one' – in 1999 O's lost to Scunthorpe United in the Play-off Final at Wembley, who scored their goal? The book is like a Leyton Orient knowledge book of information.

This quiz book is going to answer a number of my Christmas gifts this year and is top of the list for myself, having been employed by Leyton Orient from October 1966 until August 1979 within the fundraising & commercial department. My final position was Commercial Manager; I left to take up the same post at West Ham United. I made so many friends during my time at the O's and still keep in touch with them now, like Bob Mount, his family started supporting the O's in the Lea Bridge Road days, and Bob is like a walking Orient reference book. When he comes to stay with us one of the first things he says is 'Do you remember' or 'Did you know' you just know it's a Leyton Orient matter. Then there's Brian Rigby, the Rigby family are all big Orient supporters and his son was Kit Manager. Bill McClements, the police sergeant that held the supporters back when the wall come crashing down during the FA Cup game v Chelsea. We meet up and are always talking about the Leyton Orient days and always 'Do you remember'. I will never forget the Golden Goal Girls that sold tickets at home matches and sometimes at away games. I married one of them, Susan Bruce, we just celebrated our 40th wedding anniversary. Others also married Leyton Orient supporters or staff, they may not have won on the Golden Goal tickets but like me I'm sure they won in the marriage stakes.

Once you start looking at this book you will not put it down, you will be totally addicted to the questions and answers. How do I know? Well I know how professional a writer and how passionate Neil Kaufman is about his beloved Orient, a book with his name on it WILL be a great read and a success. Neil doing a Leyton Orient Quiz Book covering from 1881–2012 will be such an eye opener for every single supporter, those that visit the stadium or those that support from afar, who have now given up visiting the stadium because of age or like me have moved away from the area. Leyton Orient has many thousands of supporters that still support the O's no matter what.

I'm hoping that you enjoy this first ever Official Leyton Orient Quiz Book. Also, that you appreciate the time work and that Neil has put into it. I'm sure it will bring you and your friend's enjoyment.

Finally I would like to thank Neil for asking me to do a foreward, it's been an honour.

I will be brushing up on my knowledge of Leyton Orient's past in Lanzarote where my wife and I now live in retirement. To the supporters and club 'THANKS for the great memories of my time working at Leyton Orient 1966–79'.

Best wishes, enjoy quiz time and may Leyton Orient have a successful future.

Brian Blower
Lanzarote, Spain
August 2012

Introduction and Acknowledgements

First and foremost I give thanks to All Mighty God for giving me the opportunity of working on and finishing this first ever quiz book on Leyton Orient Football Club; in this economic climate it is becoming increasingly difficult to produce such books, so many thanks to one and all involved in making this book happen.

The idea for a quiz book on the O's came about after many requests from O's fans and even former players that I am in contact with all around the World.

I had plans to produce an updated version of my book Men Who Made Leyton Orient FC, but this had to be put on hold due to the economic recession, but as one door closes another opens.

The opportunity of a quiz book arose when one of my publishers, DB Publishing and in particular its managing director Steve Caron, talked about the concept and then commissioned me to produce a quiz book and I thank Steve and his team for their help and support in the book's production, and also to Leyton Orient Football Club for giving its blessing and support for the book.

A special thank you to Peter Kitchen, to Brian Blower, who was the person back in the early 1970s at the club to appoint me, along with chairman Brian Winston, as the club's historian and to write in the matchday programme on its history and then in 1974 the first ever book written on the club, along with Alan Ravenhill, and to Terry 'Henry' Mancini, for writing the forewords to the book, both players still have a strong affinity to the club they both starred for many years ago; 'Kitch', now retired, writing his piece while planning his next trip to some exotic place and Terry writing his piece while chilling out at his holiday home in the lovely coastal town of Kynsna in the Cape, South Africa, in July 2012 before he goes back to work.

As with my previous nine books, a special thank you to my darling wife Debbie and our twin daughters Amy and Samantha for their constant prayers, love, patience and understanding while working on these books.

This quiz book carries over 1,300 questions and answers, and has been split into 15 chapters, starting with the formation period, going through various periods of time and decades, ending with a chapter about O's playing in the various Cup competitions over the years.

Some of the questions being fairly easy, and some a little more difficult, but all done with the purpose of enlightening all O's and footballing fans around the world about our grand history and important events, and covering many of the players, some great, some not so great, and officials over the years right down to today when we all look to the Gaffer and his boys taking O's up the League.

I would love to add a final question in a second edition, who scored the goal that took O's up to the Premier League in 2015?

In the meantime while we all wait for some great milestones to unfold, enjoy this very first quiz book on the O's.

Tamika Mkandawire scores Orient's 5,000th League goal and celebrates in style, at The Matchroom Stadium on 1 September 2007 in a 2–2 draw against Northampton Town. (Reproduced with kind permission of Simon O'Connor, Leyton Orient photographer.)

Chapter 1

The Formative Years

1.   To start off the book, do you know the middle name of the author, it starts with the letter 'N'?

1A.   Which year was the club founded, 1879, 1881, 1888 or 1891?

2.   Who formed the club?

3.   What sport did the members first play, football, cricket or rugby?

4.   What name did they first play under, Orient, Star, Glyn, Eagle or Clapton?

5.   Name the club's first secretary?

6.   When did the club first take up the game of football and change its name to Orient, was it: 3 July 1883, 3 October 1879 or 3 March 1888?

7.   What other major footballing event took place that year?

8.   Why was the name Orient chosen by its committee, and who suggested the name?

9.   What were the first club colours?

10.   How did the nickname 'O's' come about?

11.   Where was the club's first ground located, Whittle Ground, Millfields Road, Glyn Road or Brisbane Road?

12. What League did O's first play in: Leyton League, London League, Cockney League or Clapton & District League?

13. When did the club change its name to Clapton Orient, was it: June 1895, June 1888, June 1898 or June 1900?

14. In April 1902 what honour did the club achieve?

15. Name O's first prolific goalscorer with 66 goals between 1897 and 1902 before he joined Luton Town?

16. In November 1902 a London League match had to be abandoned by the referee due to crowd trouble, name O's opponents?

17. When did O's turn professional, was it: July 1899, August 1901, May 1902, November 1903 or June 1904?

18. O's beat Shepherd's Bush in their first game as professionals, what was the score, was it: 1–0, 3–0, 5–0, 11–0 or 15–0 and who scored?

19. O's joined the Second Division of the Southern League in 1904, name O's first opponents, was it against: Tottenham Hotspur, Fulham, Luton Town or Brighton & Hove Albion?

20. O's had a disastrous time down at Portsmouth on 11 March 1905, what happened?

21. On 21 April 1905 O's first manager is appointed, name him?

Chapter 2

First Season in the Football League 1905–06

22.   Name O's financial benefactor, who paid all the expenses, including wages and transfer fees?

23.   During May 1905 manager Ormerod hired a hotel to sign up a number of players, in which town was the hotel located?

24.   One player who signed up was a former Irish international full-back, he had won five caps and played for Sheffield United in three FA Cup Finals. What was his name?

25.   All Football League players were on a maximum weekly wage at the time, how much was it?

26.   Name the player who scored O's first goal in the Football League?

27.   Other than for his footballing career, why is Kingaby best remembered by football historians?

28.   O's first ever League victory: who was it against, what was the score and who scored?

29.   During March 1906 O's sold a player to Chelsea for £150 to ease their financial troubles, some years later this player managed the O's for 12 years, name him?

30.   A youngster made two appearances and scored once in 1905–06. He was released by O's because the management felt he was too frail. He joined Southern League side Southend United, scoring 91 goals from 65

appearances. He joined Manchester United where he won two League titles, one FA Cup winners' medal and bagged six goals in the FA Charity Shield and also played once for England. Name the player?

31.   The best win of the season was in April 1906 4–2 against Bradford City, who scored the goals?

32.   What was the highest attendance to witness an O's game during that first League 1905–06 season?

33.   Where did O's finish that season?

34.   O's had to seek re-election at the League's AGM to stay in the League, how many votes did they gain and what happened?

Chapter 3

Up to World War One

35.   In 1906–07 one player stood out, scoring 17 goals, name him?

36.   In July 1906 O's signed 32-year-old right-half David Buchanan from Plymouth Argyle, what was so unusual about him?

37.   Who scored O's first goal of the 1906–07 season?

38.   Fred Parker came on trial in June 1907; he had the fans in fits of laughter as every time he was knocked to the ground he would be seen crawling around the pitch, and so the fans gave him a nickname, what was it and what personal playing record did he set with O's?

39.   When skipper Fred Parker led his team on to the field at Millfields Road for the opener of the 1909-10 season against Gainsborough Trinity, there was a different look about them, what was it?

40.   Although struggling on the football field, what other sport were O's crowned champions of in both 1907 and 1909?

41.   In April 1909 Tottenham Hotspur were the visitors and drew a record crowd to Millfields Road, what was the attendance?

42.   In September 1909 O's beat the eventual Division Two champions Manchester City, what was the score and who scored?

43.   A winger, Joseph Charles Dix signed for O's in June 1910 from Portsmouth, what was unusual about his transfer?

44.   O's had their best season so far in 1910–11, where did
       they finish on the Division Two table?

45.   What happened to O's in Paris on 7 November 1911?

46.   In 1911–12 a young Scotsman came into the side and
       netted 19 goals from 27 League appearances, who
       was he?

47.   In the first ever League meeting with this London team during
       December 1913 O's won 1–0, name the team?

48.   What was significant about Orient's home record in the
       1913–14 season?

49.   In February 1914 O's signed a Belgium amateur
       international player, making him the first foreigner to appear
       for O's in the Football League, who was he, and how many
       appearances did he make?

50.   In April 1914 O's went to Woolwich Arsenal and drew 2–2,
       scoring two goals in the final minutes before 35,500 fans,
       what did that mean for the Gunners?

51.   Name the only player to have played a League game in
       every season leading up to World War One, 1905–06 to
       1914–15?

52.   O's beat Leicester Fosse 2–0 on 24 April 1915 before
       21,000 fans. What was significant about this match?

Chapter 4

The War Years 1915–19

53.   How many O's players and officials went off to war?

54.   Name the three O's players killed in action?

55.   In goal for O's in a number of war games was a famous goalie from Manchester United, can you name him?

56.   Also in the team during that period was a young Irishman named Patrick O'Connell. After the war he made quite a name for himself as a manager, do you know who with and where?

57.   In the final game of the 1916–17 season, O's lost at home 8–0 to Tottenham Hotspur, what did the journalist from the Hackney Gazette do in disgust?

58.   A 17-year-old Tottenham Hotspur's amateur top scored for O's in the 1918–19 season, he later played for England and in the 1930s he played for the O's in the League, name him?

59.   During World War One, O's played a total of 148 wartime matches, scoring 157 goals and conceding 402 goals. How many matches were won?

60.   One player scored 30 goals during the war years, the most by any player, can you name him?

Chapter 5

The Twenties

61.   In 1919–20 O's signed three brothers from Scotland, can you name them?

62.   How many games did the brothers play together in an O's shirt?

63.   In October 1919 a player made a single O's League appearance, four years later he was manager of Inter Milan in Italy, can you name him?

64.   In November 1921 O's played which London club for the first time in the Football League?

65.   Both in April 1921 and April 1922, O's had two special visitors for League matches against Notts County and Bristol City, can you name them?

66.   On 18 February 1922 the O's manager died in hospital after suffering a heart attack, aged 47. Name the manager and how many years had he been with the club both as a player and manager?

67.   On 9 December 1922 at Millfields Road against Bury, a 2–0 defeat, O's had two set of brothers in their side, can you name them?

68.   During this same period O's had another set of brothers, who played 25 League games together, who were they?

69.   Owen Williams holds another O's record, what is it?

70.   Albert Pape had a bizarre transfer to Manchester United on 7 February 1925, what was it, and how much did they pay?

71.   Name the player who scored his only League goal in April 1925 from 139 League games, he left in June 1927 for Southend United?

72.   Scotsman Charlie Rennox left O's in 1925 to join Manchester United for £1,250. He had a most unusual first name, do you know what it was?

73.   Name the player who was top goalscorer in the 1925–26 season?

74.   After a run of 225 consecutive League and Cup games over five years, goalkeeper Arthur Wood missed the match at Blackpool on 11 December 1926 due to a thigh strain, who replaced him and what was the result?

75.   There was another player making his League debut at Blackpool who in later life played cricket for Essex, was an MP for Chelmsford for 14 years and was made a knight of the British Empire, name him?

76.   Seven days after the loss at Blackpool and with Wood back in goal, O's faced Reading at home, what was the result?

77.   Between 1926 and 1931, O's had on their books a very famous Kent and England wicketkeeper/batsman; who was he and what was his cricketing record?

78.   During January 1927 O's signed a forward from Plymouth Argyle, who two years earlier had bagged 47 goals in 25 appearances during an FA tour to Australia, who was he?

79.   On 2 April 1927 O's lost at home to Portsmouth 4–5 in the side was Jack Rutherford, what was significant about his age?

80.   Who was O's top goalscorer is season 1926–27?

81.   What record was achieved in the 1926–27 season?

82.   What major sporting event took place at O's Millfields Road ground on Wednesday 28 August 1928?

83.   On 18 March 1929 O's entertained Tottenham Hotspur, what was the result and the attendance?

84.   What happened to O's at the end of the 1928–29 season?

85.   What was O's first match in Division Three South?

86.   How did O's do at the end of the 1929–30 season?

87.   When O's played their final League match at Millfields Road who was it against and what was the score?

88.   How many years had O's played at Millfields Road?

Chapter 6

The Thirties

89. In July 1930 O's were forced to move to a new ground, where was it?

90. Name the player who kicked off the 1930–31 season in fine fashion?

91. After a match with Torquay United on 8 November 1930 the visitors reported the club to the Football Association, stating that the wooden fence was too close to the touchline. What was the result of the FA's investigation?

92. What three games were played away from Lea Bridge Road and where?

93. What were attendance figures for the two League games?

94. Which player ended the 1930–31 season in fine fettle and how many goals did he net for the season?

95. In the 1930–31 season which London team was faced for the first time, losing 3–0 away and winning 2–1 at home?

96. Name the player in 1931 who scored O's 1,000th goal in the Football League?

97. On 14 April 1931 who took over from Peter Proudfoot as secretary-manager?

98. Do you know what his salary was?

99. Arthur Wood made his final O's appearance at Newport County on 2 May 1931, how many appearances did he make?

100.   Name the goalkeeper who took over from Wood in goal the following season?

101.   Who was O's top marksman in 1931–32?

102.   O's signed right-winger Frederick John Sidney Le May from Watford in August 1932, what is he best known for?

103.   In season 1932–33, O's had two players with the same surname, who were they?

104.   A Scotsman who made his name in American soccer with the Chicago Yugoslavs and Chicago Bricklayers, spent two seasons with O's between August 1931 and May 1933, who was he and show his record?

105.   Name the O's player who won a Welsh cap in November 1933 against England?

106.   In later life Mills lived in Bristol, how did he die?

107.   In 1934 O's hit Aldershot Town for what record League score, was it: 7–1, 8–1, 8–3, 9–1 or 10–1 and who scored the goals?

108.   David Halliday was one of the most prolific goalscorers in the history of the game at 0.751 goals per game, even higher than the great Jimmy Greaves (0.691 per game). He joined O's on 29 December 1933 for £1,500, how did the 36-year-old perform for O's in his first season?

109.   It's quite a feat for a player to be ever-present in a League season, O's had two players in 1933–34, who were they?

110.   In the 1934–35 season one player couldn't get a look into the League side but he did make one appearance in the FA Cup, who was he?

111.   Who opened the 1935–36 season with a hat-trick and went on to become O's leading goalscorer, breaking Richard McFadden's record of 21 goals in 1914–15?

112.   The Lea Bridge Road Ground had an official capacity of 20,000; for the visit of Millwall on 13 March 1937, what was the attendance?

113.   O's survived having to apply for re-election by the skin of their teeth in 1932–33, having just won eight games all season, how did it end?

114.   In May 1931 why were O's suspended from the Football League?

115.   Due to the financial instability manager Jimmy Seed resigned, what club did he join?

116.   Whose money helped save the O's from closure?

117.   Name the chairman at the time of this financial crisis?

118.   Name the player, and his age, who joined O's from Liverpool in June 1933, having made 366 senior appearances for the 'Pool'?

119.   In July 1933 O's signed one of the most prolific goalscorers in the history of the Football League, who was he?

120.   In January 1934 O's thrashed Southend United 5–2 before 8,091 fans, who scored O's goals?

121.   Who netted 19 goals from the final 21 League appearances in 1933–34?

122. On 28 December 1935 O's lost 5–3 at Luton Town, who scored the goals for the Hatters?

123. In the 1936–37 season O's had two sets of players with the same surnames, who were they?

124. Who ended up with 25 League and Cup goals for the 1935–36 season?

125. 1936–37 was to be the last season at the Lea Bridge Road ground, how many years did O's play there?

126. Who did O's play in their final League game at Lea Bridge Road and when?

127. What was the attendance for this match?

128. In that match Ambrose 'Bud' Rossiter scored twice in the 3–0 victory, what was unusual about him?

129. The final League match that season was a 1–1 draw at Brighton & Hove Albion on 1 May 1937, but it was not happy for Rossiter, why?

130. In July 1937 O's moved to a new ground, where was it?

131. Which amateur club played at that ground previously, for over 30 years?

132. Who did O's face in their first match at the new ground and what was the score?

133. What was the attendance for this match?

134. Name the goalscorer of O's first goal at the new ground?

135.   Was this the first Football League match ever to be held in Leyton?

136.   After moving to Leyton in 1937 what was the club's name?

137.   In O's first League win at the new ground, who scored a hat-trick?

138.   What the highest home League attendance of the 1937–38 season?

139.   Who made just a single League appearance in 1937–38?

140.   O's avoided having to apply for re-election after beating Swindon Town in the penultimate League fixture of the 1938–39 season, what was the score?

141.   Who scored O's final goal of the 1938–39 season in the 1–1 draw at Port Vale on 6 May?

142.   Who ended as O's top marksman that season and how many goals did he score?

143.   Who was O's secretary-manager for the start of the 1939–40 season?

144.   O's signed their first coloured player, can you name him?

145.   What decision was taken by the FA on 3 September 1939 about the 1939–40 season?

146.   Name the three teams O's played before the season ended?

147.   Can you list the results of these three League matches?

148.   There were six players who played in those three games, who had their playing records expunged, so 'officially' never appeared for O's in the Football League, can you name them and show their playing records?

149.   Goalkeeper John Ellis was famous when appearing in a match for Bristol Rovers against Luton Town in 1936, what was it?

150.   William McFadyen was a real hotshot with both Motherwell and Huddersfield Town, what record does he still hold for the Scottish side?

Chapter 7

The War Years 1939–46

150A. O's beat Watford 2–1 in the very first wartime match on 1 October 1939, who scored the first goal?

151. On 21 December 1940, O's travelled to White Hart Lane to play Tottenham Hotspur but had a few players short and borrowed one Spurs youngster to play, who was he?

152. O's signed a Jewish-born player from Tottenham Hotspur in 1938 but he only played in the war years making 11 appearances with one goal between 1940 and 1942, name him?

153. O's went to play Arsenal on 8 February 1941, what was the score: 10–2, 11–2, 15–2 or 17–2?

154. Can you name the player who scored 10 goals for the Gunners in this game, six being headers?

155. Name the 16-year-old spotted by O's playing on Hackney Marshes in 1940 who later represented England Amateur side at the 1948 Olympic Games obtaining a bronze medal, and was rated one of the top amateur players of his era?

156. Which Barking-born centre-half after making 110 wartime appearances for Leeds United played for O's in 1941?

157. Between 12 October 1940 and 25 April 1941 O's played 20 wartime matches, how many goals did they concede and what was their playing record?

158.   Name the player with the unusual surname who joined O's from Ipswich Town in 1941 and later starred for Bradford City in the Football League?

159.   Name the former Millwall winger who made nine appearances for O's in 1941–42?

160.   Who was the midfielder who joined O's from Wrexham and made 55 wartime appearances with 13 goals?

161.   Name the South African born left-winger who with Aberdeen netted 53 goals from 95 Scottish League and Cup appearances and then made 166 appearances with Plymouth Argyle? He later played two wartime games for O's.

162.   O's signed a player in 1942, he scored 53 goals from 100 appearances for Hartlepools United, who was he and what was his playing record with O's?

163.   Another humiliating result for O's occurred in February 1942 at Portsmouth, what was the result, 10–1, 11–1 14–1 16–1 or 18–1? Also, one Pompey player bagged eight goals in this game, who was he?

164.   During the seven years of wartime football only one player bagged four goals in a match for O's, who was he and who was it against?

165.   Name the former Middlesbrough and Brentford player who joined O's in 1940 and played for two seasons but made only three appearances due to being away on active service?

166.   Which former Scottish international player previously with Manchester City and Ipswich Town joined O's in 1942, and what was his O's playing record?

167.   Name the goalkeeper who made over 200 League appearances for Arsenal but made a single wartime appearance for O's in 1943?

168.   Between 1943 and 1945 a young player made 33 appearances for O's, scoring eight goals, he later went on to become one of the great Welsh footballers, who was he?

169.   Name the Bolton Wanderers player who joined O's in February 1944 and made 45 wartime appearances with three goals for O's?

170.   In the 1944–45 season O's had two players who both later became O's managers, name them?

171.   Which O's player made the most appearances in the war years between 1939 and 1946, and how many games did he play?

172.   Name the famous Crystal Palace set of brothers who appeared for O's during the war years, their surname beginning with the letter 'D'?

173.   Which player scored the most goals for O's during the war years?

174.   Name the goalkeeper who made 63 wartime appearances for O's between 1942–45, and later played for both Fulham and Reading?

175.   Name the Scotsman from Partick Thistle who netted a hat-trick for O's against Watford on 20 January 1945?

176.   Name the forward who scored a hat-trick in the 5–3 defeat at Walsall in September 1945 before 5,000 fans?

177.   Who was the defender born in Peshawar, India in 1914; he
         made over 90 League appearances with both Plymouth
         Argyle and Brighton & Hove Albion and appeared in 32
         wartime appearances, scoring once in 1944–45 for O's?

178.   During September to January 1946 a former Tottenham
         Hotspur and England player managed O's, name him?

179.   Why did he have to leave O's?

Chapter 8

1946 to 1949

180.   League football commenced again on 31 August 1946. How many seasons had O's played in the Football League before World War Two?

181.   Name the O's manager in August 1946?

182.   What were O's home colours during that 1946–47 season?

183.   Who were O's first home opponents on 31 August 1946 and what was the score and attendance?

184.   Name the O's goalscorers?

185.   In the side that day was a centre-half named Kenneth James Fenton. He made seven League appearances but did something unusual the following March. What did he do?

186.   On 20 September 1946 Hewitt resigned as secretary-manager, why?

187.   Who took over from Hewitt?

188.   How long did the new manager remain in charge?

189.   What was his record?

190.   Who replaced him?

191.   Name the former O's player who was the assistant secretary?

192.   What change occurred at O's on Wednesday 2 October 1946?

193.   Hewitt's first match back in charge was against Mansfield Town on 12 October 1946, what was the result?

194.   Name the goalkeeper who made his only O's League appearance at Northampton Town in a 4–1 defeat during November 1946?

195.   What injury did he receive in the match?

196.   What happened to him after leaving O's?

197.   Who made the most League appearances for O's that 1946–47 season and what was his total?

198.   O's avoided having to seek re-election by winning 3–1 at Mansfield Town, what part did defender Cyril Bacon play?

199.   Name the player who made his only League appearance in the final game of the season at Cardiff City before 24,572 fans?

200.   How old was he on his debut?

201.   What was very unusual about the Cardiff City match?

202.   Name the player who scored most goals in the 1946–47 season?

203.   Where did O's finish that season?

204.   Name the Essex businessman elected to the O's board of directors in 1947?

205.   In the 1946–47 season what were O's new colours?

206.   Who scored O's first goal of the 1947–48 season?

207.   Name the goalkeeper in the side that day in a 1–1 draw at home to Crystal Palace?

208.   Name the player signed from West Ham United in November 1947 for £2,000, he had one of the hardest shots around?

209.   In January 1948 a 34-year-old centre-half was brought into the side due to injuries, this being his only game of the season, who was he?

210.   For the visit of Ipswich Town on 26 March 1947 the match attracted a then record Brisbane Road crowd, what was it?

211.   Frank Neary played a significant part in helping O's avoid seeking re-election at the end of the season, what was it?

212.   In April 1948 O's appointed a new manager, who was he?

213.   In Football League history what is McBain famous for?

214.   Where did O's finish that season?

215.   Who were ever-present in the 1947–48 season?

216.   Frank Neary hit 25 League goals in the 1948–49 season, whose record did he break?

217.   Which visiting goalkeeper was knocked unconscious for a full 30 minutes from one of Neary's shots in 1948?

218.   What did Torquay United do to poor O's in April 1949?

219.   What number League match was it?

220.   Who was in goal for O's that day and where was he born?

221. A few years later he appeared at Wembley, what was the occasion and who did he play for?

222. How many times had O's conceded six goals in the League prior to this first 7–1 defeat by Torquay United?

223. What was the only goalscoring highlight of the 1948–49 season?

224. In June 1949 who was appointed chairman of O's?

225. Who was the new chairman's first appointment?

226. What was significant about this appointment?

227. Stock signed a Scotsman named George Burns Sutherland from Partick Thistle, what record did he achieve during the 1949–50 season?

228. Who was it against and what were the scores?

229. Frank Neary was sold during October 1949 for £7,000, who did he join?

230. Name the Scottish born full-back who made his only League appearance of the season at Aldershot during October 1949?

231. Name the club he joined O's from?

232. O's conceded seven goals twice in the 1949–50 season, who inflicted the pain for the first time during October?

233. Who was in goal that day for O's, was it Gerula, Welton, Groombridge or Hobbins?

234. What was the attendance for that match?

Chapter 9

The Fifties

235. Which team scored seven goals against O's at Brisbane Road in February 1950?

236. In that match name the visiting player who scored five goals?

237. Name the goalkeeper between the sticks that day?

238. In the final match of the season at Southend United in May 1950, O's needed a point to avoid seeking re-election and the home side had to win to gain the runners-up spot, meaning more money for them. What happened in the final few seconds of the game?

239. O's ended on 35 points, which teams ended one point behind them?

240. Which Welsh international did O's sign for a then record fee in July 1950 from Tottenham Hotspur and what was the fee?

241. Who top scored for O's in the 1950–51 season and show his playing record?

242. Which player was ever-present that same season?

243. Name the famous England Amateur international player who signed for O's in November 1950 and later had a number of years with both Chelsea and Walthamstow Avenue?

244.   What was O's best win in the 1949–50 season, was it:
         3–1, 4–1, 5–1, or 6–1 and who was it against?

245.   Due to an injury crisis for the penultimate match of the 1950–51
         season at Newport County, O's had to call upon the trainer to
         play at right-back, who was he and what was his age?

246.   Which O's player ended the 1950–51 season as the
         second top goalscorer?

246A.   Name the former O's player who was appointed
         groundsman in July 1951 and stayed for 16 years?

247.   Name the Irish born player on loan from Leicester City in
         November 1951?

248.   How many League appearances did Bruce make for O's?

249.   What was O's best result in the 1951–52 season, was it:
         4–0, 5–0, 6–0, 7–0 or 8–0 and who did O's beat?

250.   Who scored O's goals?

251.   Who top scored for O's in the 1951–52 season, was it
         Rees, Harris, Pacey or Jackson and how many goals were
         scored?

252.   Which player was transferred to Liverpool during November
         1951?

253.   What were the terms of that transfer deal?

254.   Due to poor weather, O's match on Thursday 24 January
         1952 at Walsall attracted what attendance?

255.   What was the score?

256.   Name the player who was ever-present during the 1951–52 season?

257.   O's matches, in fact all sport in London was postponed during early December 1952, why?

258.   O's beat Aldershot 4–1 on 25 April 1953, who scored?

259.   Pacey ended the 1952–53 season with a bang against Colchester United, what did he do?

260.   Pacey ended as top goalscorer, how many League goals did he score: 16, 17, 18, 19, 20, or 21?

261.   Which goalkeeper made the most League appearances in the 1952–53 season?

262.   Stan Charlton played in all 46 League games, how many goals did he score: 0, 1, 2, 3 or 4?

263.   O's finished with the most points since League football re-commenced in 1946 after World War Two, how many points?

264.   Name the 37-year-old full-back who joined O's in July 1953 from Southampton after making 223 appearances for the Saints?

265.   Name the Canadian born player who joined O's in July 1953?

266.   What was O's highest home League attendance of the 1953–54 season and who was it against?

267.   How many own-goals were scored by O's opponents during the 1953–54 season and who scored them?

268.   Which player ended on 15 League and Cup goals in 1953–54?

269.   How many penalties did Ken Facey convert in the 1953–54 season and who were they against?

270.   Name the O's youth player who in 1953 joined the O's backroom staff at 15 years of age and three years later became assistant secretary; a few years later he became the youngest club secretary in the Football League with another London club, which club was it?

271.   Who scored O's opening goal of the 1954–55 season?

272.   During September 1954 O's drew 2–2 at Coventry City, who scored O's goals?

273.   O's went to Exeter City during November and thumped the home team, what was the score, was it 4–1, 5–1, 6–1, 7–1 or 8–1?

274.   Who scored a hat-trick in that game?

275.   What was the significance of the result at Exeter City?

276.   Between October and December 1954 O's played 10 League games; how many goals did they score, was it 12, 18, 22, 26, 29, 31 or 35?

277.   Name the player who scored four goals against Exeter City during March 1955?

278.   How many penalties did Ken Facey convert in the 1954–55 season?

279.   How many penalties did he miss that season, and who were they against?

280.   Where did O's finish in Division Three South during the 1954–55 season?

281.   How many goals did O's score that season?

282.   What was significant about their League total?

283.   Who were crowned as Division Three South champions?

284.   Name the Welshman who became a teacher at Leyton County High School and made his O's debut in April 1955?

285.   O's beat Colchester United 6–0 on 8 September 1955, one of the goals was an own-goal by someone who in later years became an O's manager, name him?

286.   The following week O's beat Coventry City 3–1, one was an own-goal, who scored it?

287.   In November 1955 what shock news did O's fans read in their morning newspapers?

288.   What was the fee received?

289.   What effect did this have on the attendance for the next home match against Crystal Palace?

290.   In that match, O's beat Crystal Palace by a big score, was it: 6–0, 7–0, 8–0, 9–0 or 10–0?

291.   What did this result mean?

292.   Who scored two goals on debut in the victory over Brentford in January 1956?

293. Julians had joined O's in June 1955 from which club, was it: Tottenham Hotspur, Arsenal, Walthamstow Avenue or Nottingham Forest?

294. Which Scotsman did O's sign from a Welsh club during February 1956?

295. What was the value of the deal to get him to sign for O's?

296. What was the value put on Burgess?

297. Who paid the transfer fee out of their own pocket, was it: Alec Stock, Arthur Page, Harry Zussman or Leslie Grade?

298. Who suggested O's sign the Scotsman?

299. Name the station where he actually signed, was it: Paddington, Victoria, Newport or Leyton?

300. Name the manager who signed him, was it: Stock, Gore or Carey?

301. In February 1956 what happened to Alec Stock?

302. How long did he stay there?

303. What did he tell the press on his return to O's?

304. In the 7–1 victory over Queen's Park Rangers in March 1956 two players scored all the goals, name them and how many did each get?

305. In the 8–3 win over Aldershot on 17 March 1956, who scored O's goals?

306. In the six League matches during March 1956, how many goals did O's score, was it: 5, 11, 16, 19, 21 or 25?

307. In the end O's beat which club to be crowned champions of Division Three South, was it Ipswich Town, Millwall, Brighton & Hove Albion or Southend United?

308. What was the result and who scored the goals?

309. What was unusual about the first goal?

310. What did this O's team achieve that season for the first and only time in its history?

311. Two players scored more than 20 goals that season, who were they? Either Hartburn, Heckman, Johnston, Julians or Woosnam?

312. When O's gained promotion to Division Two in 1955–56, was this O's first, second, third or fourth time they had gained promotion?

313. What significance did the number 17 play at the end of the Championship winning season?

314. Who scored O's goal on the opening day of the new Second Division campaign in a 1–4 home defeat to Nottingham Forest?

315. Who did he join O's from and what was the transfer fee?

316. O's gained their first win of the 1956–57 season during September with a home win over Bury, what was the score: 4–0, 4–1, 4–2 or 4–3?

317. Later that month O's came up against a rampant Stoke City away and lost, what was the result: 4–1, 5–1, 6–1, 7–1 or 8–1?

318. After a year in the reserves, this former Arsenal player made his O's League debut in April 1957, who was he?

319.   During the 1956–57 season how many goalkeepers did O's use and what were their total League appearances?

320.   Where did O's finish after their first season back in Division Two after a gap of 20 seasons?

321.   How did O's start the 1957–58 season?

322.   Name the manager in charge at the time?

323.   Which two O's players represented a London XI away to Lausanne Sports XI in the first-leg of the Inter-Cities Fairs Cup (the forerunner to the UEFA Cup) semi-final on Monday 16 September 1957? London lost 2–1.

324.   Name the player who broke his leg at Fulham in October 1957 and never played again?

325.   What was his career record for O's during his three seasons with the club?

326.   What did the O's do to help him financially?

327.   Due to a fixture against West Ham United being postponed on Saturday 15 February 1958, because of the Hammers involvement in the FA Cup, O's played a friendly against a Yorkshire team whom they had not met for 32 years, name that team and the score and goalscorers?

328.   Tommy Johnston smashed his own O's League goalscoring record in 1957–58, how many goals did he score?

329.   On 2 March 1958 what did Johnston do?

330.   How many League goals did Johnston score that season?

331.   Mark Lazarus signed for O's in November 1957, how many League games did he play in the 1957–58 season?

332.   In March 1958 who re-joined O's for a third spell?

333.   O's scored a total 77 League goals in the 1957–58 season, how many did the two leading goalscorers net between them?

334.   What competition did O's win on 6 May 1958?

335.   Who did O's beat in the early rounds and then in the Final?

336.   Can you name the O's team who played in the Final?

337.   Name the two players who scored on their League debut in a 3–3 draw at Swansea Town during September 1959?

338.   What first name was Hasty known by during his footballing days?

339.   Len Julians; who did he leave O's for in December 1958, and for how much?

340.   Which Irish born player scored four goals for O's in November 1958 and who was it against?

341.   Which O's player won a Welsh cap in November 1959 just before being sold to West Ham United?

342.   How much did the Hammers pay for him?

343.   In later years what was he famous for?

344.   Who did O's sign in January 1959 for £6,000 and from which club?

345.   In what game did he make his debut?

346.   Why was this friendly played in January 1959?

347.   Which player returned to O's on 14 February 1959 for
        £7,500?

348.   In March and April 1959, in two home League games O's
        scored a total of 12 goals, who did they beat and by what
        score?

349.   Who scored the goals over this period?

350.   Eddie Baily had a famous nickname, do you know what it
        was?

351.   Which players ended as the top League goalscorer for the
        1958–59 season?

352.   Who was the manager in charge for the 1959–60 season,
        was it Stock, Carey, Sexton, Gore or Baily?

353.   Name the player in October 1959 who scored on debut
        direct from a corner-kick?

354.   Which Charlton Athletic player scored an own-goal for O's
        in November 1959, and 12 years later played in the
        League for O's?

355.   Who scored O's final goal of the fifties' decade and who
        was it against?

Chapter 10

The Sixties

356. Name the former Arsenal player who scored his only goal for O's during January 1960?

357. Which famous American singer attended the O's versus Aston Villa match on 13 February 1960?

358. What did the players ask from him and what did he do?

359. Ken Facey converted eight penalties in the 1959–60 season, but how many did he miss and against whom?

360. On the final day of the 1959–60 season in a 2–2 draw at Middlesbrough, Both Eddy Brown and Tommy Johnston scored O's goals, what was significant about their goals?

361. O's signed a player from Sheffield Wednesday, who was the son-in-law of the famous Manchester United manager Sir Matt Busby, who was he?

362. What was his full name?

363. What was significant about the match against Brighton & Hove Albion on Wednesday 31 August 1960?

364. What was the score, the scorers and attendance for this historic match?

365. What was the cost to install the floodlights?

366. In September 1960 which goalkeeper was forced to retire through injury at the age of 30?

367.   What was his O's playing record?

368.   Name the goalkeeper who came in to replace him?

369.   Which club did he join from and what was the transfer fee?

370.   Which Welsh born player made two League appearances during December 1960?

371.   Which Canadian born player joined O's from Gillingham in January 1961?

372.   What was the highest League attendance to watch an O's match during the 1960–61 season?

373.   What was the score in this defeat at Anfield, was it 1–0, 3–0, 4–0, 5–0 or 6–0?

374.   What player scored a hat-trick that day for Liverpool?

375.   Name the 18-year-old who moved to West Ham after only making 4 (1) League appearances for O's, scoring one goal?

376.   What was unusual about Sealey's only goal for O's?

377.   Name the player who joined O's in part exchange for Sealey?

378.   Which manager signed the deal on behalf of the Hammers?

379.   Dunmore was not O's first choice Hammer's player; who did manager Gore want in the Sealey swap deal, but what was his decision?

380.   With the season coming to a close O's had to beat Norwich City to avoid relegation, what happened?

381.   Who scored O's goal?

382.   What was significant about his goal?

383.   How many League and senior Cup goals did Johnston score for O's?

384.   Johnston made his final League appearance for O's at Lincoln City on 29 April 1961, which two players made their O's League debuts that day?

385.   What was the connection between Johnston and Taylor?

386.   Who made the most appearances in the 1960–61 season?

387.   Which player retired at the end of the 1960–61 season after nine seasons with the club and what job did he take?

388.   What was Ken Facey's playing record with O's?

389.   Where does Facey feature on O's all-time top goalscoring charts?

390.   What record did Facey hold at the time?

391.   Name the former Everton manager who was appointed O's boss on Tuesday 1 August 1961?

392.   Name his two first-team coaches?

393.   On a sweltering hot day O's went to Walsall, who were unbeaten at home for 16 months in September 1961; what was the result?

394.   Who were the goalscorers?

395. Manager Carey made his first signing in February 1962; who was he and what was the transfer fee?

396. He made his debut against Sunderland, what did he do?

397. Carey made another signing the following month; who was he and what was the fee?

398. So, in a short period of time O's had paid out £21,000 in transfer fees, where did the money come from?

399. In October 1961 O's went to Anfield to play Liverpool, what was the score?

400. Who scored for O's with a cracking shot from fully 40 yards?

401. In the 1–0 win at Brighton & Hove Albion during April 1962 full-back Eddie Lewis missed the game through injury, who replaced him?

402. O's went to Luton Town for the penultimate game of the season and won 3–1, which player came up trumps for O's?

403. Due to injuries in their team Luton fielded a goalkeeper at centre-forward, who was he?

404. The dramatic final game of the 1961–62 season was all about beating Bury and seeing if Sunderland dropped points at Swansea Town, how did O's do?

405. How did Sunderland fare in Swansea?

406. Name the player whose two goals took O's up to the top tier of football?

407.   He only played because of an injury to another player, who was that player?

408.   What was the attendance of the Bury match?

409.   What did the fans throw up into the air when they heard O's were promoted?

410.   Who were O's promoted with?

411.   Was this the first time O's had played in the top tier of football?

412.   For the 1962–63 season in the top flight, how many players did manager Carey sign?

413.   Which team did O's play in their first match in the top tier and what was the result?

414.   What was the attendance?

415.   Name the player who scored O's first goal in the top tier?

416.   Who did O's beat to gain their first win in the top flight?

417.   Score and scorers please?

418.   O's went to Everton and lost 3–0, but what was significant about the attendance?

419.   Later in September 1962, O's beat at home two of the top clubs in English football, who were they and what were the scores?

420.   Who scored against Manchester United?

421.   Name the scorers against Everton?

422.   What were the attendances for these two matches?

423.   O's lost at home 1–5 to Tottenham Hotspur during October 1962, name the goalkeeper, a solicitor by profession and England amateur international, who made his O's debut?

424.   What was the attendance for the visit of Spurs?

425.   In November 1962 O's gave a debut against Ipswich Town to which former England youth international player and what was his age?

426.   What did he do in this game?

427.   What was he known as during his playing days?

428.   O's signed a winger from West Ham United on 20 December 1962, who was he and what was the transfer fee?

429.   On debut against Birmingham City, what did he do?

430.   After the defeat by Spurs back in October, how many League games did O's play until their next victory?

431.   Who did they beat and what was the score?

432.   In March 1963 O's signed a new player, who was he and from which club did he join?

433.   Which club was he on loan with at the time of his transfer?

434.   What was his transfer fee?

435.   Mason stayed for a further season and made a total of 24 League and Cup appearance, but how many goals did he score?

436.   O's gained their sixth and final victory of the season in May 1963, who was it against and what was the score?

437.   Who was the unlikely scorer of the winning goal, and how many other goals did he score that 1962–63 season?

438.   O's were relegated in bottom place, how many points did they finish with?

439.   When Director Leslie Grade asked manager Carey, 'how much it would take to keep O's in the top flight?' What was Carey's reply?

440.   What was O's average home attendance in the top flight?

441.   Who ended the 1962–63 season as O's top goalscorer?

442.   Were any players' ever-present throughout the 1962–63 season, if so give their playing record?

443.   In July 1963 Carey resigned as manager, which club did he join as boss?

444.   Who was appointed acting manager?

445.   For the start of the 1963–64 season which player was signed from Arsenal and for how much?

446.   Which Portsmouth player scored six goals against O's during the two matches played in the 1963–64 season?

447.   What were the results against Portsmouth?

448.   In the 6–3 defeat, which O's player scored his only goal of the season?

449.   Who missed a penalty for O's in that match?

450.   Who was appointed O's manager in November 1963?

451.   Name the player sold to Norwich City on 16 March 1964 and for what fee?

452.   What player was signed on the same day to replace Bolland and for what fee?

453.   During the season which two pop groups entertained the O's crowd before matches and during half-time?

454.   To avoid relegation O's beat which Welsh side during April 1964 and what was the score?

455.   Can you name the three famous Welsh footballers in the visitors side?

456.   During April 1964 which loyal servant received a testimonial match playing against a former Leyton Orient XI, having to retire through injury?

457.   What was his playing record with O's?

458.   How did O's open the 1964–65 season?

459.   Who scored a hat-trick?

460.   Which 18-year-old scored on his debut in that same match?

461.   Another O's youngster made his League debut in that match, who was he?

462.   Four days later, what happened to O's in Manchester and what was the result?

463.   At the end of August 1964 there was a turnaround against the same Manchester team, what was it and who scored O's goals?

464.   On 12 September 1964 O's went to Swansea Town and seven goals were scored in the match, what was the result and who scored for O's?

465.   A week later against Rotherham United Ted Phillips scored one of the most remarkable goals seen at Brisbane Road, what was it?

466.   After a run of seven matches without a win, manager Fenton was fired, who took over?

467.   Who was signed a few days later, from which London club and what did that player do?

468.   Which Scottish born player made a single appearance in the 1964–65 season?

469.   In the final seven games of the 1964–65 season, what did O's do to avoid relegation?

470.   Which former O's player was appointed manager for the start of the 1965–66 season?

471.   Which Hove, Sussex born youngster was signed in July 1965?

472.   Sexton signed another player born in Hove, who once netted five goals for Brighton in a League match, name him?

473.   Name the O's player who was made the youngest captain in the Football League in 1965?

474.   Name the player signed from Wisbech Town for £1,000, who scored the first O's goal of the 1965–66 season?

475.   On 4 September 1965 against Preston North End who became O's youngest ever player to play in the Football League and what was his age?

476.   Out of interest, can you name the youngest player ever to appear in a Football League match, it happened on 30 September 2008 and how old was he?

477.   Jimmy Scott was the first player to sit on the bench against Huddersfield Town on 21 August 1965 but was unused. Can you name the player who was the first O's playing sub and what injured player did he replace?

478.   Which former Tottenham Hotspur and West Ham United player joined O's in October 1965 and scored to secure a 1–0 win?

479.   In December 1965 manager Dave Sexton asked for funds for new players; he was refused, what happened?

480.   Which player did Les Gore sign from Middlesbrough in March 1966 for £2,000?

481.   Do you know where Le Flem was born?

482.   Who scored two goals to secure O's fifth win of the season at Derby County by 3–1 in April 1966?

482A.   In the same Derby match, O's had two players sent off with similar sounding names, who were they?

483.   Name the player who made his only League appearance for O's in April away at Bristol City?

484. In the final two games of the season O's played the two top teams at home, Manchester City and Southampton, how did O's do?

485. With Southampton needing a point for promotion. It was O's highest League attendance for the season, what was it?

486. O's being relegated, how many points did they end up with and how many points were they behind second from bottom Middlesbrough?

487. In June 1966 who was appointed manager to lead O's in their Third Division campaign?

488. Who was his first transfer deal, and what was the nature of this deal?

489. Who was his second transfer deal and which players were involved?

490. Who was the next major transfer that Graham did with his old club Charlton, where he was formerly a consultant, and what was the fee involved?

491. Dick Graham ended up in hospital due to an old back complaint and suffering from abdominal pain; who took charge of first-team affairs while he was away?

492. What were O's home colours for that season?

493. O's lost their first match of the 1966–67 season at Oldham Athletic by 3–1 with Dave Metchick scoring, but which player hit the woodwork twice for O's?

494. What was O's first win of the season and who was it against?

495.　Who scored O's goals?

496.　Name the player who joined from Crystal Palace but made just a single League appearance throughout the 1966–67 season and who was it against?

497.　Name the player who joined O's in November 1966 from South African club Arcadia?

498.　What event took place on Sunday 20 November 1966 at Brisbane Road and why?

499.　Name the player who joined O's from Gravesend & Northfleet in December 1966, who in later years became a famous manager?

500.　In March 1967, O's went to promotion chasing Watford and caused a sensation, what was it?

501.　Who scored twice in that match?

502.　Which full-back was moved to centre-forward against Doncaster Rovers in April 1967 due to injuries and netted a hat-trick?

503.　Which player ended as the top goalscorer for the 1966–67 season?

504.　What two major changes occurred at the club for the start of the 1967–68 season?

505.　Why the name change?

506.　For the second match of the 1967–68 season at home to Torquay United manager Graham gave debuts to two young players, who were they?

507.   How old was Taylor and was he the youngest to appear for O's?

508.   Unlike Taylor who went onto make over 100 League appearances during his first spell with the club, how many appearances did Still make?

509.   How many goals did Cliff Holton score in the 1967–68 season?

510.   Why so few goals for the prolific striker?

511.   Holton was close to netting 300 career League goals, what did he end on and how many years had he been in the game?

512.   Name the player who walked into manager Graham's office with a letter from Cliff Holton asking for a trial, having returned from playing with the Port Elizabeth club in South Africa?

513.   With Holton having retired, who ended as the top goalscorer in the 1967–68 season and how many goals did he score?

514.   In September 2012 what position did Massey hold in football?

515.   On Monday 26 February 1968 manager Dick Graham resigned, why?

516.   Who was the young player involved?

517.   Who took over as caretaker manager after Graham left and for how many matches?

518. Who was appointed as player-manager on 8 March 1968?

519. The following day, which Gillingham player scored two own-goals playing against O's, was it John Arnott, Andy Arnott or Billy Arnott?

520. In March 1968 name the player who joined O's from Coventry City on a free transfer?

521. Which player ended as the top League goalscorer for the 1967–68 season, was it Holton, Massey or Halom?

522. Which former England international did O's sign from West Ham United on 22 July 1968 and for what fee?

523. Who was in goal for the first League game of the 1968–69 season?

524. Bowtell was with O's for six seasons, how many League games did he play?

525. On 10 August 1968 who was the man who first introduced a new theme tune for the visit of Rotherham United and what was that tune?

526. When was the first season the O's players ran onto Brisbane Road before a match to music and what was that tune?

527. Who did O's sell to Fulham in October 1968 and what was the record outgoing transfer fee?

528. O's splashed out £18,000 on two players between October and December 1968. Who were they, which club did they join from and what was the fee?

529.   In the final game of the 1968–69 season, who did O's beat
        to ensure Division Three survival, also note the score and
        goalscorers?

530.   How many goals did centre-half Terry Mancini score during
        the 1968–69 season?

531.   Who ended the season as the top League goalscorer?

532.   What decision did Jimmy Bloomfield make for the start of
        the 1969–70 season?

533.   How many new players did Bloomfield sign for the start of
        the new 1969–70 season?

534.   Which youth player scored during August 1969 on his
        senior debut and who was it against?

535.   O's beat high-flying Fulham 3–1 in a midweek game during
        September 1969, what was the attendance?

536.   Who did Bloomfield bring back to Brisbane Road for a
        second-spell in October 1969 for £7,500?

Chapter 11

The Seventies

537. At the turn of the New Year (1970), where were O's in the League Division Three table and who was one place behind them?

538. Who scored the goal to ensure O's were crowned Division Three champions?

539. Who ended as the top goalscorer in 1969–70?

540. How many players appeared in the Championship winning season?

541. How many players were ever-present in that League campaign?

542. Can you name these players?

543. Which European team did O's face in a promotion celebration match on Monday 4 May 1970 and what was the result and attendance?

544. What award did manager Bloomfield receive at the end of that season?

545. O's opened the 1970–71 season with a wonderful 3–1 win over Sheffield United, one player had a cracking game what did he do and how did he celebrate?

546. Why was the game against Sunderland at Brisbane Road on 12 September 1970 stopped by the Referee for seven minutes?

547.   Which youth player made his League debut against Watford during November 1970 with a goal on five minutes?

548.   Another youth player made his League debut in the final game of the 1970–71 season, who was he?

549.   What did Harris become at the club in later years, was it coach, manager, chiropodist or secretary?

550.   O's scored the lowest number of goals by any team in the Second Division in the 1970–71 season, how many goals was it: 27, 28, 29, 30 or 31?

551.   What is significant about that total?

552.   Which player was the top League goalscorer that season?

553.   A lady from the backroom staff who had been with the club for over 25 years retired through ill health in 1971, who was she and when did she die?

554.   Who did O's Bloomfield sign from Manchester City in June 1971 and for how much?

555.   Jimmy Bloomfield resigned as O's manager in June 1971 and was appointed boss of which club?

556.   What did Leicester City pay O's in compensation, was it £1,000, £3,000, £5,000, £6,000, £10,000 or £25,000?

557.   What happened at the club as an aftermath to the deal?

558.   On 12 July 1971 who was appointed O's new boss?

559.   Who was club secretary, between 1971 and 1973?

560. On his home debut how many goals did Ian Bowyer score, was it: 1, 2, 3 or 4?

561. After a 6–1 defeat at Burnley on 28 September who did manager Petchey sign to bolster his defence and from which club and what was the fee?

562. 3–1 up at half-time at Bristol City on 23 October 1971, what was the final result?

563. In January 1972 which former Tottenham Hotspur player and later Spurs and Crystal Palace manager joined O's as a consultant and stayed for three years?

564. O's recorded their best victory of the season during January 1972 over Sunderland, what was the result and who scored?

565. Why did O's attract a record crowd of 33,263 fans to Brisbane Road in the final game of the season in May 1972?

566. O's scored 60 League and Cup goals in 1971–72 season, who was the top goalscorer?

567. On 22 August 1972 who did Bloomfield sign for Leicester from O's and for what record fee?

568. In September 1972 who did O's sign for a then club record fee from Crystal Palace and what was the amount?

569. Gerry Queen has been living in America for many years, do you know what he has been doing?

570. Which foreign born player did O's sign from Preston North End in December 1972 and for what fee?

571. Where was he born and when?

572. Towards the end of 1973 O's went on a fabulous home winning streak, how many games did they win, was it: 3, 4, 5, 6, 7 or 8 games?

573. Who top scored in the 1972–73 season?

574. In 1973 who took over as club secretary, having spent a number of years as assistant secretary with Crystal Palace?

575. Another backroom staff appointment was made in 1973; he was a former footballer who in season 1948–49 played for three different teams all of which won promotion, yet he never received any medals as he didn't play enough games; who was he and what did he do at O's?

576. In September 1973 O's had an excellent win at Fulham, what was the result and who were the scorers?

577. Which goalkeeper made his only League appearance at Hull City in a 1–1 draw during October 1973?

578. How was he beaten?

579. O's went to Notts County in December 1973 and won, what was the score, was it: 2–1, 3–2, 4–2, or 5–2 and who scored?

580. Gerry Queen had to leave the field, why?

581. During October and November 1973 manager Petchey went back to his old club and signed three players, who were they and what were the transfer fees?

582. In December 1973 Os had a memorable Boxing Day win over a London side before 20,611 Brisbane Road fans, who was it against and give the score and scorers?

583. The author left Leyton at midnight by coach during February 1974 with some keen O's fans to visit the very wet Cumbria to see O's play; which team did O's visit and what was the score?

584. O's played its first League match on a Sunday in March 1974, who was it against and give the score and scorer?

585. The final game of season saw O's having to beat Aston Villa to gain promotion over Carlisle United, what was the result and attendance?

586. What was average home attendance in the 1973–74 season?

587. Who was voted as O's first ever Player of the Year that season?

588. Which player did O's sign in July 1974, from Crystal Palace and for how much?

589. He was one of the smallest strikers around, what was his height?

590. Who were O's first opponents in the 1974–75 season?

591. Which player made his League debut for O's in their best win of the season during October 1974?

592. What player had a perfectly good looking header disallowed for a foul at Old Trafford in December 1974 against Manchester United to deny O's a 1–0 victory?

593.   Who scored O's final goal of the season against Southampton on 26 April 1975, was it: Queen, Bullock, Cunningham or Grealish?

593A.   What did he avoid by scoring the goal?

594.   During this season how many goalless draws were there, either: 5, 7, 9,11, 12 or 13?

595.   How many goals do you think O's actually scored in the League during 1974–75, was it: 25, 26, 27, 28, 29, 30 or 31?

596.   What player top scored that season in the League and from how many appearances?

597.   John Jackson was ever-present that 1974–75 season in goal, how many League goals did he concede that season, was it: 35, 38, 39, 40 or 50?

598.   What Championship did O's win in May 1975 and who did they beat in the Final?

599.   In July who was appointed head groundsman and how long did he stay at the club?

600.   Manager Petchey thought he had found the player to bring extra fire power to the team, what was the deal he completed in July 1975?

601.   How many goals did Allder score during the 1975–76 season?

602.   Four players made just a single League appearance that season for O's, who were they?

603.   Name the player who made three League appearances for O's, in 1975–76, all as a playing substitute?

604.   Who ended as the top League goalscorer?

605.   O's are champions again in five-a-sides, who did they beat in the Final and what was the score?

606.   Who was the Player of the Tournament?

607.   Who started the 1976–77 season as manager, was it Peter Angell, Jimmy Bloomfield or George Petchey?

608.   Name the striker signed in July 1976, from which club and what was the fee?

609.   O's lost their first three League games of the 1976–77 season without scoring, who scored O's first League goal of that season and who was it against?

610.   In a 3–0 win over Cardiff City September 1976, Laurie Cunningham scored twice, but who netted the third on debut with a great run and finish?

611.   O's introduced something new on 27 December 1976, what was it?

612.   What were the main features of the new crest?

613.   What else is featured on the new crest?

614.   Can you name the three people involved in the crest's design?

615.   How many crests had the club before this new one?

616.   Can you describe the other four crests and the years worn?

617.   Which player was transferred to West Bromwich Albion on 9 March 1977 and what was the deal?

618.   Name the two Albion players who came to O's as part of the Cunningham deal?

619.   In May 1977 which London club did O's visit, being thrashed in the first half but came out on top in the second half?

620.   Which Fulham player did all the first half damage?

621.   In the final match of the 1976–77 season against Hull City which player scored the vital goal that secured O's Division Two survival?

622.   There was a scare for O's in the match, what was it?

623.   On 6 July 1977 which former chairman died?

624.   Name the manager who signed Michael Peter Kitchen from Doncaster Rovers in July 1977, was it Petchey, Angell or Bloomfield?

625.   What was the fee paid to Doncaster for Kitchen?

626.   What happened after O's lost 4–1 at home to Blackpool on 22 August 1977?

627.   Name the Blackpool player who scored a hat-trick that evening and how long did it take him to get them?

628.   Who took over as caretaker manager after Petchey left?

629.   What was the result of Angell's first home game in charge and who was it against?

630.   Who returned to O's as manager on 12 September 1977?

631.   How many hat-tricks did Peter Kitchen score that season and whom against?

632.   Which O's record holder left the club on 9 March 1978 to join old boss George Petchey at Millwall on a free transfer?

633.   What record does Peter Allen still hold and what are his playing statistics?

634.   Name the player who made his League debut in April 1978 as a sub and who was it against?

635.   To avoid relegation O's had to win at Cardiff City on 9 May, what was the result and who scored?

636.   How many goals did Kitchen get in the 1977–78 season?

637.   What was unique about his 21 League goals?

637A.   Name the O's player sold to QPR in August 1978 and for how much?

638.   Which youth player made his O's debut in a 1–0 home defeat against Wrexham on 26 August 1978 and what was his position?

639.   Do you know where Smith was born and when?

640.   In the same match against Wrexham, five players of colour featured for O's, who were they?

641.   Which two players made their O's debuts at Charlton
         Athletic in October 1978?

642.   What did Moores do in the game?

643.   In September 1978 who came on as a sub at Blackburn
         Rovers for his only O's League appearance?

643A.   On 14 November 1978 O's played Swedish side IFK
         Gothenburg in a first-team friendly at Brisbane Road, but
         can you name, firstly the 16-year-old youth player who
         replaced the sick Joe Mayo and an American who came on
         as a sub and do you know what they are doing now?

644.   O's went to West Ham United on Boxing Day 1979 and
         caused a big upset; what was it and who scored and what
         was the attendance?

645.   With O's in seventh position on the Second Division table
         and Leicester City in 17th spot, what was the result at Filbert
         Street on 10 February 1979 and who scored O's goals?

646.   A few days later came another big surprise to O's fans;
         what was it?

647.   Who was the Fulham youngster joining O's as part of the
         Kitchen deal?

648.   Was Gray a success with O's or not?

649.   Do you know what happened to Gray after his time with
         O's?

650.   In February 1979 which player returned for a second-spell
         with O's and where from?

651.   The final game of the 1978–79 season attracted a record seasonal crowd, what was the attendance and who came to O's and won 1–0 to gain promotion?

652.   Name the player who returned to O's in May 1979 after a gap of over nine years?

653.   O's signed a new goalkeeper from West Ham United in July 1979, who was it and what was the fee?

654.   Who on 18 July 1979 sadly collapsed and died while running with the O's players in Epping Forest?

655.   What other two players, besides Day, did manager Bloomfield sign in 1979 and for how much?

656.   In October 1979 O's won their first League game of the season; who did O's play and what was the result and who scored?

657.   What do you think the attendance was for this London derby: 4,090, 5,090, 10,090, 15,090 or 20,090?

658.   Name the former O's director who died on 15 October 1979 at his holiday home in Frejus. France, aged 63?

659.   Which former Charlton Athletic player scored his only goal for O's at Preston North End during November 1979?

660.   Which player scored O's last goal of the 1970s and who was it against?

Chapter 12

The Eighties

661. Who scored O's first League goal of the new decade and who was it against?

662. O's beat Wrexham 4–0 on 2 February 1980 for their highest win of the season, but who was a special visitor that day from Australia?

663. What was O's lowest attendance of the 1979–80 season and who was it against?

664. Who was O's big name signing in July 1980 and what was the fee and which club did he sign from?

665. O's had a good win at Watford in February 1980, what was the score and who scored?

666. In the final 10 games of the 1979–80 season, how many games did O's win and what was their record?

667. How many players were ever-present in the League campaign of 1979–80 and name them?

668. The English film star Hattie Jacques died on 6 October 1981, what connection did she have with the O's?

669. Who in November 1980 did O's sign for a then club record fee and what was the amount and where from?

670. Which London side did O's convincingly beat during March 1981 and what was the result and goalscorers?

671. Where did O's finish in Division Two in the 1980–81 season?

672. Who ended the season as top League goalscorer?

673. Which two O's players represented Nigeria in 1981 and who was it against?

674. Which O's player was transferred to top-tier side Notts County and for how much and how was the amount paid?

675. What did manager Jimmy Bloomfield do soon after because of the transfer?

676. What happened then?

677. Who scored the first goal of the 1981–82 season in a victory, and who was it against?

678. How many games did O's play until their next victory?

679. What date was Paul Francis Went appointed as full-time manager?

680. What did chairman Brian Winston do on 12 October 1981?

681. How long was Went in charge for?

682. What was Went's record as both caretaker manager and full-time manager?

683. Which player was sold in September 1981, to whom and for how much?

684. Who was appointed as O's manager and when?

685. Who was appointed as his assistant the following month?

686.   When did O's win their next game, what was the score and who was it against?

687.   In November 1981 which player left O's for Brentford and what was the reported fee?

688.   What was his playing record with O's?

689.   Name the Welsh international player who scored two goals for O's on loan in December 1981 and who against and who was he on loan from?

690.   Who did O's sign from Hartlepool United in March 1982 and what was the fee?

691.   When was his first League goal for O's, and where was it?

692.   What was the attendance of that match at Stamford Bridge, was it: 5,009, 6,009, 10,009, 12,009, 15,009 or 20,009?

693.   O's finished the season in style, who did they beat and what was the result?

694.   Which player made his O's debut in that Leicester match?

695.   Where did O's finish in the 1981–82 season and with how many points?

696.   Who was the top goalscorer that season and with how many goals?

697.   Sadly, Ian Moores died from lung cancer aged just a few months short of his 44th birthday, what date did he die?

698.   What was O's lowest League attendance of the season? It was in May 1982 and who was it against?

699.   Which player was starting his 10th season with O's in August 1982?

700.   During October 1982 how many goals did Mervyn Day let in?

701.   In that same month which two players did O's sign on loan and from whom?

702.   They made their debuts at Brisbane Road against Bristol Rovers, what was the result?

703.   Who returned to O's after a spell in Hong Kong and scored the winner in his first game back, and who was it against and what was the result?

704.   In January 1983 who scored his only goal for O's?

705.   Who made a couple of appearances for O's during February 1983?

706.   Which club did this player join in June 1983?

707.   Name the former Arsenal and Crystal Palace star who joined O's in March 1983 on a non-contract deal?

708.   In the final game of the 1982–83 season O's had to beat Sheffield United at home to keep their Division Three status, what happened, show the result, goalscorers and attendance?

709.   Which team was relegated to Division Four instead of O's?

710.   Who left O's in May 1983 for £25,000?

711.   How many appearances did Mervyn Day make for O's?

712.   What job was Day doing in April 2012?

713.   Who did O's sign to replace Day between the sticks and from whom?

714.   Was he the first 'keeper' with a surname starting with the letter 'K' to play for O's, if not, who was the other goalie?

715.   In May 1993 manager Ken Knighton was sacked, who replaced him?

716.   Name the player who joined O's in August 1983 as the manager's first signing and stayed for 10 seasons?

717.   How many games did he play and goals did he score during his O's stay?

718.   O's won 4–3 at Exeter City in February 1984, what was different about one of the O's goalscorers?

719.   Who went one goal better during April 1984?

720.   Also during April 1984 a brother of a famous O's captain made a couple of League appearances, who was he?

721.   Who was O's top goalscorer in the 1983–84 season?

722.   Who made the most League appearances that 1983–84 season?

723.   What was Corbett's middle name?

724.   O's led Hull City 4–1 at home during November 1984, what was the final result?

725.   Who scored on debut during February 1985?

726.   Who scored a hat-trick for O's in April 1985?

727.   In the final game of the season, O's had to win to have a chance of avoiding the drop in to Division Four, what happened?

728.   How many times had O's previously played in the lowest tier of the Football League?

729.   What was O's average home attendance that season, was it: 1,640, 2,640, 3,640, 4,640 or 5,640?

730.   Who started the 1985–86 season as first choice goalkeeper?

731.   Which club did he join O's from, was it, Southampton, Nottingham Forest, Millwall or Charlton Athletic?

732.   Which 6ft 2in striker did O's sign in July 1985 and from which club?

733.   Who did Southend United snap up from O's on a free transfer before the start of the 1985–86 season?

734.   What did he do on his Southend debut and who was it against?

735.   For the visit of Halifax Town in April 1986, O's had one of the lowest League attendances in their history, what was it?

736.   Which player ended the 1985–86 season in great style, how and where?

737.   Where did O's finish that 1985–86 season and with how many points?

738.   What announcement did O's make in the summer of 1986?

739.   Who saved the club from closing down?

739A.   Who helped to broker the takeover deal between Wood and the Ovenden family?

740.   Who did O's sign in March 1987 for £10,000?

741.   Which O's player was the top League goalscorer for 1986–87, was it: Juryeff, Godfrey, Comfort, Jones, Shinners or Castle and how many goals did that player score?

742.   In the final game of the season, which club beat O's for them to avoid relegation down into the Conference and by what score?

743.   On 1 July 1987 what did O's change?

744.   During September 1987 what League record did Os achieve and against who and what was the score?

745.   The following month O's defeated Rochdale by what score, was it: 5–0, 6–0, 7–0, 8–0 or 9–0?

746.   Who were the goalscorers against Rochdale?

747.   Which player in 1987–88 scored 10 goals from the final nine League games?

748.   O's had to beat the Division Four champions Wolverhampton Wanderers at home to gain a place in the Play-off, what happened?

749.   What was significant about the attendance for that game?

750. Which player signed from Millwall for £25,000, yet made just three appearances for O's first team?

751. Who was assistant manager to Frank Clark in August 1988?

751A. What position did he hold in October 2012?

752. Who scored a hat-trick in O's 8–0 victory over Colchester United in October 1988?

753. Who joined from Arsenal on loan in January 1989 and scored on debut at Crewe Alexandra and made a wonderful addition to the team?

754. Name the player who joined O's in February 1989 and who played a significant part in O's history?

755. Where did O's finish in the Division Four table and what did it mean?

756. Who did O's beat in the Play-off semi-finals and what was the aggregate score?

757. Who scored O's goals?

758. Who made only his second first-team appearance in the first semi-final?

759. O's played Wrexham in the Play-off Final, how did they do in the first leg in Wales?

760. O's won the second leg 2–1 and so were promoted, who scored O's goals?

761. Who scored Wrexham's goal?

762.   Which player came on as a substitute on 17 minutes to replace the injured Kevin Dickinson?

763.   Who was the unused substitute in the second leg of the Final?

763A.   Name the player who missed the celebrations in order to rush off to Ireland by helicopter for his wedding?

Chapter 13

The Nineties

764. In the 1990–91 season which club were the first to beat O's at home and what was O's home record leading up to that game?

765. In February 1991 who scored on his first full League start for O's and who was it against?

766. How old was he on his debut?

767. What player made his League debut as a substitute in April 1991?

768. The same player became one of the most prolific goalscorers in non-League football scoring 102 goals from 184 appearances for Purfleet, but in 2012 what work was he doing since his retirement?

769. Who scored a hat-trick for O's in March 1992 and who was it against?

770. Who made his debut in the final game of the season at Fulham?

771. Who played all the games in the 1990–91 season and how many games were played?

772. Who took over as manager in July 1991?

773. Who scored all O's seven goals in the opening four League matches of the 1991–92 season and how many goals?

774. How many points did O's pick up from those four games?

775.   Who was sold to Sheffield Wednesday in November 1991 and what was the initial fee?

776.   Name the player who formed part of the deal?

777.   Which team came to Brisbane Road in December 1991 as leaders of Division Three?

778.   What was the final result?

779.   What major event happened in the match and who got sent off?

780.   Can you name the referee?

781.   Who scored on his League debut in the penultimate game of the 1991–92 season?

782.   What was O's average attendance for the 1991–92 season, was it 3,460, 4,460, 5,460, 6,460 or 7,460?

782A.   Name the player, with his full names, who joined O's in August 1992 from Frickley Colliery for £10,000 and was born in the British Military Hospital in Rintein, Germany.

783.   When O's beat AFC Bournemouth 1–0 through a Ricky Otto goal on 17 October 1992 they did something they had not done in 21 seasons, what was it?

784.   When O's went to Wigan Athletic, losing 3–1 on Saturday 21 November 1992, what was the attendance: 806, 1,806, 3,806, 5,806, 10,806 or 15,806?

785.   How many hat-tricks were scored by O's players in the 1992–93 season and who got them?

786.   Which player scored the most League goals that season and how many did he get?

787.   Where did O's finish that season and on how many points?

788.   Who left the club after 11 years service?

789.   On 9 July 1993 which player was sold for £100,000 and to which club?

790.   After a 3–2 away defeat at Port Vale on 4 April 1994, what happened?

791.   What happened next?

792.   What were their titles?

793.   How many games did they win after taking over during that 1993–94 season?

794.   Who was top goalscorer in 1993–94 and how many were scored?

795.   Who did O's beat at the start of the 1994–95 season?

796.   How many more League games did they win in that 1994–95 season and who did O's beat?

797.   To be fair, what hampered Sitton and Turner during this season?

798.   Why was there a financial crisis at the club?

799.   Who was paying all the wages at the club?

800.   How much did the club owe and what amount of money was the club losing each week?

801.   Why did Wallace pull out from taking over the club?

801A.   In October 2012 which club was Wallace chairman and owner of?

802.   When all seemed lost who came in to rescue the club in March 1995?

803.   How much did Hearn pay for the club?

804.   Name the famous short film which encapsulated the goings on at the club?

805.   Who made this film, then I will tell you about the person?

806.   The best victory of the season was 4–1 against Peterborough United in February 1995, who was it a personal triumph for?

807.   Going back to 18 February 1995 what decision did Sitton and Turner make at half-time in the match against Blackpool?

808.   How many games had Howard played and how many goals did he score?

809.   Four days later Howard signed for another League Club, which one and who was their manager?

810.   In April 1995 new owner Hearn had seen enough, what decision did he take?

811.   What was their League record when in charge?

812.   Who took over as caretaker manager?

813. How many games were they in charge for and who did O's play and show the results?

814. Who did chairman Hearn appoint as the new boss, was it: Loizou, Cockerill, Holland or Taylor?

815. How many away wins did O's achieve during the 1994–95 season?

816. No wonder O's finished bottom of Division Two, how many points did they obtain?

817. O's signed a player named Tony Kelly from Bury, what was his full name and what was the fee?

818. Who was the other Kelly who played later that season and where did he join from?

819. Name the loan player from West Ham United during September 1995 who scored on debut with a wonderful overhead kick but did not play another League game for O's?

820. O's did the unthinkable, they won 2–1 away at Northampton Town on 12 September 1995, it was their first away League victory in how many League games?

821. Who scored the winning goal?

822. How many more away League games did O's win in the 1995–96 season?

823. Which player tested positive for use of cocaine at Barnet on 25 November 1995?

824. What was the end result after his hearing the following February?

825.   What work did he later take up?

826.   How many people turned up for the visit of Scarborough on 19 March 1996 and what did it mean?

827.   Name the player who played in the final games of the season after waiting eight months to gain a work permit?

828.   Which club did he join O's from?

829.   On Sunday 26 May 1996 name the international team O's beat before 5,055 fans and what was the score?

830.   Who made and who scored the O's winning goal?

831.   O's had a nice pay-day, how much money did they make from the international game?

832.   As at 30 June 1996, did O's make a profit or a loss and what was the figure?

833.   Name the two veteran players manager Holland signed from West Ham United on 17 July 1996?

834.   How old were they both on signing?

835.   Sealey was related to another former O's player, who was he and what was the relationship?

836.   Sadly, both died at an early age, how old were they and when did they die?

837.   Another player signed, later he made a significant impact as a manager in the club's history, who was he?

838.   Which Australian born player made his League debut during September 1996?

839.   By the end of October 1996 what did O's achieve?

840.   After a 3–0 loss at Cardiff City on 26 October, what did chairman Hearn do?

841.   What was Holland's League managerial record?

842.   Who acted as caretaker manager and what was his record?

843.   In Cunningham's second game in charge O's beat Torquay United 1–0, who scored O's first goal after 360 minutes of League football?

844.   Who was appointed O's boss on 7 November 1996?

845.   Who did Taylor appoint as his assistant?

846.   During November 1996 the club started its official website, who designed and maintained this site?

847.   Who did Taylor sign for £50,000 from Peterborough United on 18 November 1996?

848.   O's signed the veteran goalkeeper Peter Leslie Shilton from West Ham United on 28 November 1996, but who returned to Upton Park as part of the deal?

849.   On his debut what O's record did Shilton set up?

850.   Shilton played his 1,000th League game in O's 2–0 victory over Brighton & Hove Albion on 22 December 1996, what Football League record did he set up?

851.   Shilton played his final League game against Wigan Athletic on 21 January 1996, what was his final career League tally?

852.   How many career League clean sheets did Shilton achieve?

853.   Which Norwegian born player made his O's debut in that Brighton game?

854.   Which former England international player made his debut for O's against Barnet on 1 March 1997 at the age of 39?

855.   On 8 March 1997 O's had a remarkable 4–4 draw at Brighton & Hove Albion, but what was the game also remembered for?

856.   In March 1997 manager Taylor brought in four new players, who were they and where from?

857.   How many players did manager Taylor use in League games during 1996–97?

858.   Which veteran player played 60 minutes for O's during August 1997 and then decided to retire from playing?

859.   Another young player started the season in the first team and was released soon after due to what was reported as misconduct, who was he?

860.   Which player played just eight minutes off the bench during October 1997 and was never seen in the first team again?

861.   On 28 December 1997 O's thrashed Doncaster Rovers 8–0, with this win how many times have O's hit eight goals in a League game?

862. In January 1998 another player played just a few minutes off the bench and then left the club, name that player?

863. On 9 January 1998 who did Sunderland buy from O's for £250,000?

864. What happened to him in his first reserve game for Sunderland?

865. Who while on loan in January 1998 from Crystal Palace played 50 minutes on debut but sustained a serious knee injury which eventually led to his retirement from the pro' game?

866. In February 1998 O's received a cash windfall, due to a 23 per cent sell-on clause when a player moved from Oxford United to Birmingham City, who was the player and what was the amount?

867. Who ended the 1997–88 season as O's top goalscorer and how many did he score?

868. Why did O's have three points docked for the season and were fined £20,000 and who was the main culprit?

869. What happened to him?

870. Who took over from him?

871. Who joined O's from Swansea City in May 1998?

872. Which Belgium player joined O's in July 1998 under the Bosman ruling after his club KFC Tielen hit financial troubles?

873.   A Scotsman on loan left O's on 8 October 1998 and an American-born player joined on the same day, who were they?

874.   Which 36-year-old Senegal born player joined O's from FC Leon in Mexico after training with O's?

875.   Who joined O's in October 1998 after winning a Sun Newspaper, Bravo TV search for a striker competition?

876.   What did O's achieve for the second time in their history?

877.   Who did O's see off in the semi-finals?

878.   Which goalkeeper made some brilliant saves in the second leg at Rotherham to take the match to a penalty shoot-out, was it Ashley Bayes or Scott Barrett?

879.   During the penalty shoot-out, who scored O's penalties in the 4–2 success?

880.   O's lost in the Final at Wembley Stadium 1–0 to Scunthorpe United, who scored their goal?

881.   What was the Wembley attendance?

882.   Was this the first time O's had appeared at Wembley Stadium?

883.   Who signed for O's in June 1999 with the unusual forename, and which club was he playing for in August 2012?

884.   What did the tribunal fix his transfer fee at, was it £15,000, £25,000, £35,000, £40,000 or £45,000?

885.   Name the player, who signed for O's 27 May 1999, played just 3(3) League and Cup games but was released that November because he became homesick and had a mental block when playing, and so couldn't focus?

885A.   Can you name which club he joined in June 2012?

886.   Name the South African born player signed from Southend United in June 1999?

887.   Do you know what he was working at in 2012?

888.   Name the two loan players early in the 1999–2000 season whose surname both started with the letter 'H'?

889.   Name the foreign born player who came to O's on trial in October 1999 and stayed for two seasons?

890.   How did the Croatian get to England?

891.   Which player did O's sign in November 1999 after a month's trial and what was his nickname?

892.   Who returned to O's on 12 December 1999 to boost the goalscoring fire-power, what was his reported fee and from which club?

893.   In what away victory did Izzy Christie score his first League goal?

894.   Who scored a hat-trick in that same game?

895.   How many League victories did O's gain leading up to the year 2000?

Chapter 14

2000 to 2012

896.   Who scored O's first League goals of the new Millennium and where?

897.   Towards the end of the 1999–2000 season O's played five youth players in the League, can you name any two of them?

898.   Which one of the five is now playing in the Championship and with whom?

899.   Do you know what happened to Jay Murray?

900.   Which Australian born player joined O's from West Ham United on loan in August 2000?

901.   After some wonderful displays and goals, his season long loan was cut short at Brisbane Road, why?

902.   O's secured a Play-off spot with a 2–0 victory at Macclesfield Town, who scored the goals?

903.   In the first leg of the semi-final at Hull City, who scored the only goal of the game?

904.   How did the second leg go?

905.   Where was the Play-off Final held?

906.   Who scored for O's after just 27 seconds?

907.   At the end O's lost the Final by what score?

908.   How many foreign born players played for O's in 2000–01, who were they and where were they from?

909.   Who had a testimonial against Tottenham Hotspur in July 2001 that attracted 6,636 fans?

910.   Name the French born defender who trialled for O's in that testimonial match?

911.   Who scored the opening goal of the 2001–02 season at Cheltenham Town and how?

912.   Leo Constantine had a penalty saved at home to Rushden & Diamonds on 15 September, but what happened straight after?

913.   After four straight defeats manager Tommy Taylor resigned, who took his place?

914.   Who scored the winner at Swansea City in the new manager's first match as boss?

915.   O's had a 5–0 win over Lincoln City on 22 December 2001, what happened over the next five League games and give details?

916.   Where did O's finish in 2001–02 season?

917.   After signing this player from Northwich Victoria for £50,000 in December 2000, he was released in August 2003 on a free transfer to Lincoln City having played just 13(11) League and Cup appearances, scoring two goals; who was he?

918.   Why and how did he obtain his double-barrelled name back in June 2004?

919.   Who did O's sign on a free transfer from Lincoln City in May and also on loan from Charlton Athletic in August 2002?

920.   Who on 21 October 2002 came on loan from West Ham United?

921.   Who did O's sign from Hull City on 28 January 2003?

922.   Wayne Montague Purser joined O's from Barnet in March 2003, what did he do on debut to excite the fans and who was it against?

923.   Who else made their O's debut's in that Boston game?

924.   In June 2003 which O's player gained two international caps for Northern Ireland and who was it against?

925.   On 6 September 2003 O's lost 2–1 at Torquay United, but what else occurred during the match?

926.   After just one win from the first 10 League games of the 2003–04 season, who left O's and how?

927.   Who took his place?

928.   What did he do on his departure?

929.   How did Ling fare in his first match in charge and who was it against?

930.   In a 2–1 win over Southend United during February 2004, who scored O's goals?

931.   Whose headed goal at York City on 1 May 2004 saved O's from a drop into the Conference securing a 2–1 win?

932.   After a 4–1 win over Shrewsbury Town on 16 October 2004, where did the three points take O's on the League Two table and when last did they achieve this?

933.   O's had a exciting 4–3 win at Lincoln City on 23 October, who scored a hat-trick?

934.   This was a personal triumph for him, why?

935.   Name the player who had an unimpressive loan debut in a 1–2 home defeat by Grimsby Town on 15 January 2005 and what actually happened?

936.   Who made three substitute appearances for O's in April 2005?

937.   Who was voted O's Player of the Year for the 2004–05 season and why?

938.   Which player had to retire during the season from playing due to heart problems and was given a coaching role with O's?

939.   The start of the 2005–06 season meant that the O's were starting how many seasons as members of the Football League, was it their 60th, 70th, 80th, 90th or 100th season?

940.   Who signed from Scottish side Livingstone in July 2005 on a two-year deal?

941.   Which player scored on debut after just 65 seconds in a 2–1 win over Macclesfield Town on 6 August 2005?

942.   The second O's goal in added time by Efe Anthony Echanomi was a rather cheeky affair, what did he do?

943.   What was manager Ling named (no rude comments please) in October 2005 and why?

944.   At the end of 2005 where were O's lying on the Division Two table?

945.   Who did O's sign in January 2006 from Swansea City for £40,000 and also a defender from Notts County?

946.   From 14 February 2006 to 6 May O's lost just once from 16 League games, who beat O's during that run and what was the score?

947.   It was a nervy day on 6 May 2006 with a fight between O's at Oxford United and Grimsby Town home to promoted Northampton Town to see who gained the third promotion spot, with three minutes into stoppage time it looked like Grimsby's day, but what twist happened to turn the day from tears to joy?

948.   Out of 1,938 away matches since entering the Football League in 1905, what number away victory was the Oxford win?

949.   Who was the Grimsby Town manager at the time?

950.   Which O's goalkeeper won his only cap for Wales on 27 May 2006 and who was it against?

951.   Which player left O's for Fulham on 11 July 2006 for an outgoing record transfer and what was the amount?

952.   How many League appearances did he make for Fulham during his time at Craven Cottage?

953.   Who did O's sign on a five-week loan from Bristol City on 27 July 2006?

954.   Was this the first time this same player was on loan with O's?

955.   Who scored O's first League goal of the 2006–07 season, on what time and who was it against?

956.   Which former O's player on 8 August 2006 recorded the 500,000th Football League goal when playing for Huddersfield Town?

957.   Which O's player had a successful operation for testicular cancer during October 2006?

958.   On 7 December 2006 where did O's find themselves on the League One table and on how many points?

959.   Eight days later O's went to League leaders Nottingham Forest, what result did O's achieve?

960.   Who scored the goals?

961.   Do you know Cordon's actual first name?

962.   During January 2007, O's released four players, can you name them and who they joined?

963.   Three went on free's, so which one of the four left for a fee?

964.   After a successful loan spell from Hull City in 2006, how much did O's pay for Alton Anthony Thelwell on 1 January 2007?

965.   Who made his O's League debut on 23 January in a 1–4 home defeat to Brighton & Hove Albion?

966.   What was he doing in 2012?

967. During February 2007 O's signed Ryan Jarvis on a three-month loan deal from Norwich City. What did he achieve at Millwall on 16 February?

968. Who scored two goals in this match?

969. O's won at Bradford City 2–0 on 21 April 2007 to ensure League One survival, who scored and on what times?

970. Who was in goal for Bradford City and what links did he have with O's?

971. In the final League game of the season at Huddersfield Town on 5 May 2007, which three youth players sat on the bench?

972. How many of the three players came on to make their League debuts?

973. On 5 July 2007 which player joined Nottingham Forest for a reported fee in the Nottingham press of £200,000?

974. How many appearances did he make and goals scored, and what O's record does Lockwood still hold?

975. On 1 July 2007 O's signed four players, who were they?

976. Melligan was always known as J.J. but what were his actual forename and middle name?

977. O's signed Adam Mark Boyd from Luton on 23 July 2007, what was the fee? A free transfer, £10,000, £20,000 or £50,000?

978. Boyd scored on debut in a 2–1 win at Southend United, who else scored on debut and how?

979. What was the significance of Tamika Mkandawire's goal on 57 minutes against Northampton Town on 1 September 2007?

980. Which loan player from Tottenham Hotspur scored his only League goal for O's in January 2008 and who was it against?

981. Which Portuguese born player made his O's debut as a playing substitute during April 2008 and who were the opponents?

982. How many League penalties were converted in the 2007–08 season and by whom?

983. Who was the top goalscorer for O's during this season?

984. Who was the only player to make 50 League and Cup appearances during the 2007–08 season?

985. Which player made all his 14 League appearances as a playing substitute in 2007–08?

986. Simon Wayne Corden was released by O's in May 2008, which club did he join three months later?

987. Name the four players who joined O's on free transfers on 1 July 2008?

988. Who signed on loan from Tottenham Hotspur in August 2008?

989. Who scored O's first League goal of the 2008–09 season?

990. O's signed which striker from West Ham United in September 2008 on a one month loan, making his debut from the bench against Stockport County?

991.   How many more League games did he play during his loan spell?

991A.   Name O's greatest ever player who sadly died on 4 September 2008. After hearing this news, what did the O's do?

992.   Which striker did O's sign on 23 October 2008 for a three-month loan period from Luton Town, but stayed longer?

993.   With O's in 21st position in League One, who left O's in January 2009?

994.   Who took over and for how many games?

995.   David Beckham's advisor and a former O's youth player, led a consortium to buy O's, who was he?

996.   Was the offer successful?

997.   Which Southern based club did O's beat for the first time in January 2009 and what was the score?

998.   Name the striker who came on loan from Luton Town, stayed for three months and managed not a single goal, and how many appearances did he make?

999.   On 5 February 2009 who was appointed O's manager?

1,000. How did his O's side fare early on after 10 games?

1,001. During February 2009 Jason Demetriou won two caps for Cyprus, who did he play against?

1,002. Simon Richard Church joined O's on loan from Reading, making his debut at Hartlepool United in a 1–0 win on 21 February 2009, what milestone did he record?

1,003.   In the 3–1 victory at Carlisle United on Tuesday 10 March 2009, how many passes were made leading up to O's second goal from Scott McGleish and how long did the move last?

1,004.   Who scored a brace in the 2–2 draw with Leeds United in April 2009?

1,005.   There was a dispute over the scorer of the first goal, why?

1,006.   Which Northampton Town player, who later played for O's, scored an own-goal against O's during April 2009?

1,007.   Which player made the most League appearances during the 2008–09 season, was it: Tamika Mkandawire, Jason Demetriou, Stephen Purches or Adam Chambers?

1,008.   Who scored most goals during that season?

1,009.   Where did O's finish in the League One table for 2008–09?

1,010.   What was the ground capacity of the Matchroom Stadium for the start of the 2009–10 season, was it: 8,271, 9,271, 10,271 or 11,271?

1,011.   On 23 June 2009 which foreign born striker did O's sign and where was he born?

1,012.   Name the young winger from Tottenham Hotspur who O's took on loan in August 2009?

1,013.   In the 3–3 draw at Yeovil Town during August 2009, he came up with something special, what was it?

1,014.   Who had to leave the field against Colchester United in October 2009 on 4 minutes and 29 seconds and who replaced him?

1,015.   On 15 January 2010 O's signed two loan players on one month loan deals, who were they and where were they from?

1,016.   How many games did they play for O's?

1,016A.   Name the club Adams joined in June 2012?

1,017.   Name the Frenchman who scored his first goal for O's in a 5-0 win over Bristol Rovers in February 2010?

1,018.   After the Rovers match, which player had his contract terminated after a row with manager Williams because he was not chosen ahead of Jimmy Smith as a sub replacement for Nicky Adams on 77 minutes?

1,019.   Who scored on 88 minutes to secure a point at home to Leeds United during February 2010?

1,020.   On 25 March 2010 two more players came in on loan, who were they and where were they from?

1,021.   Although Lichaj was born in Downers Grove, Illinois, USA, name the other country he could have represented and why?

1,022.   Who left the club on 3 April 2010 with the team in the relegation zone?

1,023.   Who was in charge for the match at Southampton two days later as caretaker manager?

1,024.   Who was appointed O's manager that same evening?

1,025.   What length was his contract and what was the mandate given him by chairman Barry Hearn?

1,026.   How did he perform?

1,027.   Who did he manage between 1995 and 1996?

1,028.   What award did he win in May 2007

1,029.   Who ended top goalscorer for 2009–10 and how many did he get?

1,030.   Having saved O's from relegation, what was Slade's reward?

1,031.   What young player did Slade sign on the same day in May 2010?

1,032.   Where was this youngster born?

1,033.   Which player moved overseas to ply his trade on 2 June 2010?

1,034.   What player was signed five days later, was it: Forbes, Dawson, Revell, Butcher or Omozusi?

1,034A. Name the former O's striker who sadly died on 1 August 2010 after a two year battle with pancreatic cancer?

1,035.   O's signed Michael William Liddle on a five month loan from Sunderland on 5 August 2012, where was he born and how many League games did he play for O's?

1,036.   Which Tottenham Hotspur player joined O's in September 2010 on an eight-month loan?

1,037.   Although born in Kinshasa, Democratic Republic of Congo, which country does he represent?

1,038.   Which player on loan from Millwall during October 2010 played just 45 minutes at Hartlepool United before returning to the Den due to an ankle injury?

1,039.   Which player joined O's the same day on an initial three-month contract, having been with O's on loan previously from Charlton Athletic in 2006?

1,040.   Which player scored a rare penalty in October?

1,041.   Name the sturdy full-back O's signed on loan from Brighton & Hove Albion on 28 October 2010?

1,042.   Name the Welsh International goalkeeper who joined O's on loan on 19 November 2012 and from which club?

1,043.   Two former O's players died during December 2010, can you name them both?

1,044.   During January 2012 O's signed two players on loan from Tottenham Hotspur, who were they?

1,045.   In January 2011 O's recorded arguably their best League win of the season, what was the score and whom was it against?

1,045A. Which player had his contract cancelled by mutual consent on 31 January 2011?

1,046.   In March 2011 who was charged with a number of offences of investment fraud?

1,047.   Which former O's youth player returned to the club on a two-month loan on 11 March 2011 from Crystal Palace?

1,048. In April 2011 which former O's transfer record holder scored an own-goal for O's while playing for Peterborough United?

1,049. During October 2006 O's had on trial his brother, who was he?

1,050. O's had one of their better seasons, where did they finish in League One?

1,051. During the season did O's manage to get higher than seventh on the table?

1,052. Who made the most O's appearances in 2010–11?

1,053. Who scored the most goals during the season?

1,054. Which player had the most goal assists in 2010–11, was it: Charlie Daniels, Stephen Dawson or Dean Cox?

1,055. Who was voted O's Player of the Year for the 2010–11 season?

1,056. Who was O's youth Player of the Year?

1,057. Which club was prevented from approaching O's gaffer Russell Slade on 27 May 2011 for their vacant managerial position?

1,058. On 1 June 2011 O's released six players who were they?

1,059. Which one of the six retired from the game to take up a job as a physical instructor with Virgin Active?

1,060. Which Irish utility player joined O's from Hartlepool United on a two-year deal on 16 June 2011?

1,061.   What was unveiled in the village of Fleurs, in the Somme, Southern France in July 2011?

1,062.   Which midfielder was signed to replace departing Adam Chambers to Walsall, in July 2011?

1,063.   How did O's start their 2011–12 League campaign, how many games did O's win from the opening 10 games?

1,064.   Which player in September 2011 phoned Russell Slade asking to train at O's after leaving Ipswich Town and ended up with a three-month contract?

1,065.   When was O's first League win and who was it against?

1,066.   What did O's do during October 2011?

1,067.   In the 1–1 draw with Sheffield United on 22 October, what time did Kevin Lisbie score O's goal?

1,068.   Which player netted his first League goals for O's at Yeovil Town on 25 October?

1,069.   Which O's player had his contract terminated on 24 November 2011 and why?

1,070.   Who left O's initially on loan to AFC Bournemouth after being with the club two years?

1,071.   Daniels joined the Cherries permanently on 1 January 2012 on a three and half year deal, what was the reported fee as reported in the local Bournemouth press?

1,072.   At the end of November who put pen to paper to stay with the club?

1,073.   Who converted two penalties in the 3–0 victory over Exeter City on 10 December?

1,074.   What player scored the goal that defeated League One leaders Charlton Athletic 1–0 on 31 December 2011?

1,075.   On 2 January 2012 Lee Cook scored the winner against which team?

1,076.   During January O's signed three players until the end of the season, one being on loan, who were they?

1,077.   Which player did O's sign as an emergency loan from Southampton on 9 February 2012?

1,078.   On 18 February 2012 who replaced Butcher in goal after he was stretchered off on 89 minutes against Scunthorpe United with O's losing 1–3?

1,079.   Name the former O's midfielder who was a commentator on Scunthorpe Player for the game and is a regular commentator for them?

1,080.   What did Ryan Dickson pick up in a space of minutes at Oldham Athletic on 27 March 2012?

1,081.   During end March and April 2012 O's were dragged into the relegation battle, what was their League record over this period?

1,082.   O's were saved from a relegation battle on the penultimate game of the season; who scored for Notts County at Wycombe Wanderers with the final shot of the game to send Wycombe down, losing 3–4?

1,083.   What striker did O's sign on loan from Crystal Palace on 1 March 2012 until the end of the season?

1,084.   What was his record with O's?

1,085.   How many shots did he get on target and saved?

1,086.   Which two players did O's sign on loan on 8 March 2012?

1,087.   Which player signed a short-term development contract with O's on 8 March 2012?

1,088.   How many League games did Jamie Smith play and how much time did he spend on the pitch?

1,089.   Who scored a brilliant solo goal on his first League start in the final game of the season of the 2011–12 season in a 2–1 win over Rochdale?

1,090.   Which two youth strikers made their senior debuts as playing substitutes in the same Rochdale match?

1,091.   Which other League club's youth team did Lobjoit play for as a 13-year-old?

1,092.   How many goalkeepers did O's use for the 2011–12 season and who were they?

1,093.   Which goalkeeper only sat on the bench during the 2011–12 season and who did he join in July 2012?

1,094.   Who was voted O's player of the year for 2011–12?

1,095.   Who made the most appearances for O's in 2011–12 and how many were made? And who did he join in July 2012?

1,096.   Who netted the most goals during the season and what was his total?

1,097.   Who signed for O's on a free transfer on Saturday 12 May 2012?

1,098.   Can you name the place where Sawyer was born?

1,099.   Is he the first player named Sawyer to wear an O's shirt?

1,100.   Who did O's sign from Port Vale on 19 May 2012 and what award did he win when with them?

1,101.   What country has Griffith represented during both June and July 2011?

1,102.   Which former long-time club employee died on Sunday 6 May 2012?

1,103.   Which former O's defender, now 39 years old, after being released in April 2012 by Boston United started the Active Soccer Academy in Sheffield?

1,103A.   Firstly, name the person who has been the chairman of the O's Supporters Club these past 18 years and also name his deputy and who has been promoting the heritage of the club to local communities?

1,103B.   Name the 62-year old former O's star full-back who was appointed first-team coach at AFC Bournemouth in June 2012, and later as caretaker manager?

1,103C.   Name the musician in June 2011 who named his daughter's second name as Orienta, reflecting her Chinese heritage and his support of the O's?

Chapter 15

O's in Cup Competitions

1,104.   In 1898–99 season which Cup did O's compete in?

1,105.   They beat which devilish team in the first round?

1,106.   Which two Cups did O's win in April and May 1902 and who did they defeat?

1,107.   Do you know the year that the FA Cup was first conceived?

1,108.   Who were O's very first FA Cup opponents and when?

1,109.   What was the result and who scored O's first FA Cup goal?

1,110.   In October 1904, O's were taken to an FA Cup away replay by which local club and what was the score?

1,111.   Who knocked out O's in the FA Cup Fourth Qualifying Round in 1904 and by what score?

1,112.   In 1905 O's beat three local rivals during FA Cup rounds, who were they and by what scores?

1,113.   O's reached the First Round proper for the first time, who did they play?

1,114.   The first tie at Millfields Road ended 0–0, what happened in the replay?

1,115.   Why did O's refuse to play in the FA Cup in the 1907–08 season?

1,116. On 21 September 1907 O's were ordered to field their first team against Custom House in the FA Cup and on the same day their reserve side in a League Division Two fixture at West Bromwich Albion, what were the two results?

1,117. On 19 October 1907 O's played a team called Old Newportonians in an third qualifying round FA Cup tie, what was the score and where was this club located?

1,118. In the fourth qualifying round O's were draw at home to Southern League side Southend United and drew 1–1, which O's player made his only senior appearance in that match?

1,119. In the replay O's lost 3–1, which former O's player scored the Shrimpers first goal?

1,120. In the final minute of the Southend tie O's goalkeeper Walter Whittaker had to leave the field and was taken to hospital with concussion, who went in goal for 68 seconds?

1,121. If O's had won the Southend Cup tie, who would they have played in the next qualifying round? Was it, Walthamstow Avenue, Ilford, Millwall, the 4th Battalion King's Royal Rifles or Clapton?

1,122. In 1910 what Cup competition did O's first play in?

1,123. In the 1912 London Challenge Cup Final which side did O's beat and what was the score?

1,124. In the FA Cup tie against Woolwich Arsenal on 14 January 1911 why did the 13,416 fans light newspapers in the second half?

1,125. The tie was re-played again on the following Monday afternoon before 9,519 fans, who scored first?

1,126.   Who won the FA Cup tie and what was the score?

1,127.   On 13 January 1912 O's lost a close game to Everton 2–1 in a first round tie, what happened that evening?

1,128.   On 11 January 1913 O's were thrashed at Sunderland, what was the score, 3–0, 4–0, 5–0, 6–0, or 7–0?

1,129.   This Sunderland match was one for the record books, why?

1,130.   Can you name the O's goalie that day?

1,131.   In January 1915 O's played at Southern League side Millwall. Before 16,900 fans, O's lost 2–1, but what else happened near the end of the game?

1,132.   In January 1923 another tie against Millwall, this time at Millfields, with the Lions winning 2–0, what was significant about the attendance and what was it?

1,133.   In January 1924 it took three attempts to decide the first round tie against Swansea Town, how did it end and where was it played?

1,134.   In 1925–26 O's had their finest Cup run to date. In the fourth round they beat Middlesbrough 4–2 before 24,247 fans, which former O's star was in the Boro team that day?

1,135.   In the FA Cup fifth round on 20 February 1926, which First Division side did O's beat and who scored O's goals and what was the attendance?

1,136.   In the quarter-finals, how did O's do?

1,137.   On 26 January 1929 O's were drawn at Aston Villa in a fourth round tie, how did they do and what was the attendance?

1,138.   What happened in the replay?

1,139.   In 1929 O's battled in the first round of the FA Cup against Southern League side Folkestone Town, how many games did it take for O's to get through and what was the result of the final tie?

1,140.   In the next round O's went to Newcastle United, how did they do and what was the attendance?

1,141.   In November 1930 O's drew at Luton Town 2–2, what happened to O's legendary goalkeeper Arthur Wood?

1,142.   In the replay at Highbury, which O's lost 4–2, who played in goal and what was he famous for when with Aberdeen?

1,143.   In February 1934 a new Cup competition was introduced for Division Three Northern and Southern teams, what was it called?

1,144.   Who were O's first opposition in the competition and what was the score?

1,145.   In December 1935 O's lost at Chester 3–1; which reserve player made his only senior appearance for O's in this FA Cup tie because six forwards were injured?

1,146.   In January 1936 O's beat which London team who were going great guns at the time, no it wasn't Arsenal, and what was the score?

1,147.   What was significant about the attendance and what was it?

1,148.   O's only victory in the Southern Section Cup came on Wednesday 28 October 1936, who did O's beat, what was the result and who scored for O's?

1,149.   O's played Queen's Park Rangers in the Southern Section Cup on Thursday afternoon, 11 November 1937, but with goalkeepers Charlie Hillam feeling unwell with flu and Jacob Iceton injured, O's had no goalie, what did they do and what was the final result of the game?

1,150.   The first FA Cup tie at Brisbane Road in December 1937 was against which team, what was the score and attendance?

1,151.   After the war the FA Cup in the 1945–46 season was played as a two-legged affair. O's played amateurs, Newport Isle of Wight; how did they do over the two Cup ties?

1,152.   Who scored O's goals in the first leg victory?

1,153.   O's lost in 1949 to Southend United 2–1 in the Final of what new competition?

1,154.   Along the way in that same competition that year they beat which team 7–1?

1,155.   Can you name the O's goalscorers?

1,156.   During November and December 1951 who did O's beat in round one of the FA Cup after three attempts?

1,157.   Who scored a hat-trick on his senior debut to secure a 5–4 victory over Gorleston at Highbury?

1,158.   In the next round it took a replay against Wrexham to progress to the next round, who scored the goals?

1,159.   In the third round who did O's dispose of at the second attempt, show the score and attendance?

1,160.   Who scored the O's goals?

1,161.   In February 1952 it was off to Birmingham City in the fourth
          round, who won and who scored?

1,162.   What was the attendance?

1,163.   Because O's and both Everton and Birmingham all wore
          blue, who did O's go to borrow their red shirts from?

1,164.   Who did O's play in a home fifth round tie and what was
          the result and attendance?

1,165.   In the 1953–54 O's had another exciting FA Cup run. In
          round four which London side did O's beat and what
          player scored the winner in a rare first-team
          appearance?

1,166.   The gate receipts for this Cup tie were £3,481, but what
          was the final profit made?

1,167.   In the quarter-final O's were up against Port Vale before a
          31,000 Brisbane Road sell out, who scored the goal that
          knocked O's out of the Cup?

1,168.   Which former O's goalkeeper made a brilliant last minute
          save from a George Poulton thunderbolt to take Port Vale
          through?

1,169.   On 20 November 1954 O's went to Frome Town in a first
          round tie and won 3–0, who scored O's third goal?

1,170.   On 19 November 1955 O's beat which team 7–1?

1,171.   Who scored a club record five goals in this game?

1,172.   A new Cup competition, considered by the FA as a first-team competition, was started in October 1955, was what it called?

1,173.   O's first game in the competition was a 1–0 win at Queen's Park Rangers on Monday 31 October 1955 before 2,790 fans, who scored O's goal?

1,174.   In the team that evening was an inside-forward who made over 150 reserve appearances for O's but could never break into the first team, what was his name and who did he join in 1958?

1,175.   On Tuesday 2 October 1956 O's played at West Ham United in the Southern Floodlight Cup before 14,500 fans, what was the result and who scored for O's?

1,176.   In O's side that evening was a Maltese born right-half on trial with O's, can you name him and who did he play for in later years?

1,177.   In January 1959 who scored O's two goals in a 4–2 FA Cup defeat at Blackburn Rovers?

1,178.   Which former O's player netted one of Blackburn's goals?

1,179.   On Monday 7 December 1959 O's lost an exciting Southern Floodlight Challenge Cup match against West Ham United at Upton Park by 4–3 with 8,606 in attendance, who were O's goalscorers?

1,180.   One could say it was an O's goalscoring feast, who scored West Ham's goals, they all had O's connections?

1,181.   Which player made the most appearances in the Southern Floodlight Challenge Cup for O's, was it: Sid Bishop, David Groombridge, Ken Facey, Tommy Johnston or Stan Charlton?

1,182. Who scored the most goals in this Cup competition, was it: Jimmy Andrews, Eddy Brown, Ken Facey, Tommy Johnston, Eddie Lewis or Terry McDonald?

1,183. October 1960 saw O's first ever match in the newly introduced Football League Cup, who did O's face and what was the score?

1,184. Who scored O's first goal in the competition?

1,185. In the home replay O's won 1–0 against Chester, who scored the goal?

1,186. On 7 January 1961 O's won at Gillingham in an FA Cup round three tie, what was the score, 4–2, 5–2, 6–2 or 7–2 and who scored the goals?

1,187. In round four O's were drawn at Southampton, who had beaten the Division Two leaders Ipswich Town 7–1 in the previous round; what was the score and who scored?

1,188. In round five Sheffield Wednesday came to the capital and won 2–0, but one of the goals was rather controversial, what happened?

1,189. In the League Cup during October 1961 O's lost at Blackpool by what score, was it: 3–1, 4–1, 5–1 or 6–1?

1,190. In February 1962 O's unluckily went out of the FA Cup, losing at home 1–0 in a replay to which First Division side, this after a 1–1 away draw, name the team?

1,191. What was the score in a League Cup home defeat of Chester during October 1962, was it: 6–2, 7–2, 8–2, 9–2 or 10–2?

1,192. Can you name the goalscorers?

1,193. Name the player who made his only first-team appearance for O's in that Chester Cup tie?

1,194. Who beat O's 2–0 in the fifth round of the League Cup on 3 December 1962?

1,195. Why did O's have to wait over two months to play Hull City in the FA Cup at the end of 1962 and early 1963?

1,196. After eventually disposing of both Hull City and Derby County in an FA Cup run in during 1963, who knocked O's out of the FA Cup on 16 March 1963 and by what score?

1,197. Who was the Man of the Match in O's exciting 3–2 third round FA Cup tie victory in January 1964 at Leicester City?

1,198. Who scored O's fastest ever FA Cup goal with a header to give O's the lead against West Ham United on 25 January 1964 and what time was the goal scored?

1,199. How tall was he?

1,200. Which player equalised for the Hammers, he later played for O's?

1,201. What was significant about the attendance at this Hammers Cup tie?

1,202. How did O's fare in the FA Cup replay at Upton Park?

1,203. On 6 January 1968 O's played at West Midlands League side Boston United, what was the result and attendance?

1,204. What was unusual about O's goal?

1,205.   Which O's player was booed by the Boston home fans for wearing gloves on the bitterly cold day?

1,206.   O's won the replay 2–1, who netted O's goals?

1,207.   Whose great headed goal sent Bury packing in the FA Cup third round during January 1968?

1,208.   In O's run of five FA Cup ties during 1967-68, O's were unchanged for all the games, except for one playing substitute, who was that player?

1,209.   During August 1968 O's knocked out Gillingham in the League Cup after a replay, how many goals did Vic Halom net in the two games, was it: 1, 2, 3, 4, or 5?

1,210.   A Roy Massey goal knocked out which London team in round two of the League Cup during September 1968 and what was the score and the attendance?

1,211.   O's had a great FA Cup third round victory in January 1971, who was it against, what was the score and who scored?

1,212.   In the next round how many times did O's face Nottingham Forest and why?

1,213.   O's financial coffers were swelled over the ties, what were the total attendances for those games?

1,214.   1971–72 saw O's have a great FA Cup run; after disposing of Wrexham 3–0 in round three they went to Leicester City, managed by former O's boss Jimmy Bloomfield, what was the score, who scored and what was the attendance?

1,215.   O's faced Chelsea in round five, and found themselves 2–0 down before a big Brisbane Road crowd of 30,329 fans; who scored O's third and winning goal in the final seconds?

1,216.   In round six Arsenal were the visitors to Leyton and won 1–0, watched by 31,768 fans, but why were the Gunners dubbed 'Lucky Arsenal' after this match?

1,217.   Who scored O's goal in the Final of the London Challenge Cup against Dagenham in 1972 which ended 1–1?

1,218.   Who scored the O's goals in the 2–1 London Challenge Cup Final replay victory against Dagenham?

1,219.   In January 1973 O's lost 1–4 to Coventry City in a third round FA Cup tie, who scored O's goal from the penalty spot, being his only senior goal for O's?

1,220.   What was unique about O's FA Cup ties against Portsmouth during January 1974?

1,221.   What happened in the second replay against Portsmouth and where was it played?

1,222.   What new competition was introduced in August 1974?

1,223.   What was O's first match, the result and attendance?

1,224.   Name the young winger who made his senior debut that day?

1,225.   Who scored O's very first goal in the Texaco Cup and who was it against and the score?

1,226.   O's entered another competition in August 1976 featuring teams from across the border, what was it called?

1,227.   In the group stages during August 1976 which London sides did O's defeat and what were the scores?

1,228.   Who scored O's first goal in this competition against Fulham?

1,229.   Who scored O's winner in this game?

1,230.   Who scored O's goals in the win against Chelsea?

1,231.   In the two-legged quarter- finals which Scottish team did O's defeat?

1,232.   What were the results in these games?

1,233.   In the two-legged semi-final O's defeated another Scottish side, who was it?

1,234.   What were the scores and goalscorers?

1,235.   Name the young O's goalkeeper who was on the bench for the game at Partick and where was he born?

1,235A. Who did O's face in the two-legged Anglo-Scottish Cup Final?

1,236.   O's drew 1–1 in the first leg at Brisbane Road, who scored O's goal?

1,237.   Can you name the Forest full-back marking Possee?

1,238.   Something unusual happened during the first game, what was it?

1,239.   O's lost in the second leg in Nottingham, What was the score: 2–0, 3–0, 4–0 or 5–0?

1,240. In September and October 1976, O's played Millwall three times in the League Cup, the third tie was played at Highbury, who won?

1,241. Which former O's player scored one of the Lions' goals?

1,242. Whose goal in August 1977 knocked Fulham out of the League Cup at Craven Cottage?

1,243. In January 1977 O's also played a marathon FA Cup tie against Darlington; it went to a second replay, what was the final result and who scored the goals?

1,244. In August 1977 name the O's goalkeeper who played all three Anglo-Scottish Cup games?

1,245. In 1977–78 O's had a fantastic FA Cup run in the first Cup tie, who was it against and who scored the goals in the two ties?

1,246. Who was O's next scalp in round four and who scored?

1,247. In round five against Chelsea whose wonder save in the final minutes earned a replay?

1,248. In the Chelsea replay which O's player scored the opening goal?

1,249. Who scored two glorious goals to secure O's a semi-final place?

1,250. Who did O's play in the semi-final at Stamford Bridge?

1,251. What was the score, the attendance and gate receipts?

1,252. In August 1979 which former O's player scored for Wimbledon in a penalty shoot-out to knock O's out of the League Cup, this after saving a spot-kick from Mervyn Day?

1,253.   O's last match in the Texaco Cup was a 1–0 victory during
           August 1980, who was it against and who scored the goal?

1,254.   Whose goal saved O's blushes to earn a 1–1 draw in the
           FA Cup at Altrincham on 5 January 1980?

1,255.   Which loyal O's fan sadly died in his sleep the following
           night on 6 January?

1,256.   In the 2–1 replay win over Altrincham, who scored O's
           200th goal in the FA Cup to secure a 2–1 victory?

1,257.   On 26 January 1980 O's lost to West Ham United 2–3 in
           the FA Cup; name the goalkeeper who played his only first-
           team game for O's that season?

1,258.   In 1981 name the competition that replaced the Texaco
           Cup?

1,259.   Who was O's first match in the competition against, and
           what was the result and goalscorers?

1,260.   O's lost 4–1 at Watford on 14 August 1981, who scored
           O's goal?

1,261.   O's played six matches in this competition between 1981
           and 1982, how many did they win?

1,262.   In 1983 a new competition was introduced as a forerunner
           to today's Johnstone's Paint Trophy, what was it called?

1,263.   How many games did O's play in the competition?

1,264.   Who were their opponents, also what were the scores and
           goalscorers?

1,265.   Can you name O's player-coach whose only first-team call up, due to an injury crisis, was to sit on the bench at Wimbledon in the FA Cup during November 1983?

1,266.   In 1984–85 O's reached the semi-final of the Southern Area competition, who did O's face and what was the final result?

1,267.   Who missed two penalties for O's in the shoot-out against Newport County?

1,268.   Name the O's goalkeeper playing that evening?

1,269.   In December 1986 O's lost at home 1–5 to Brentford in the Freight Rover Trophy, who hit four goals for the Bees?

1,270.   The match attracted one of the lowest attendances at Brisbane Road for a first-team game, do you know what it was, either: 649, 749, 849, 949, 1,049 or 1,149?

1,271.   On 19 January 1988 O's lost in a penalty shoot-out to Colchester United in a Sherpa Van Trophy first round tie, after the game ended 1–1. How did the shoot-out go?

1,272.   Which player came on as a substitute in the game for a rare first-team appearance and missed one of the shoot-out penalties?

1,273.   In January 1989 an O's player named Jones scored in the 3–1 win at Aldershot in the Sherpa Van Trophy, what was his full name?

1,274.   On 9 January 1990 O's lost to which team in a Leyland DAF Preliminary round Play-off game?

1,275.   Who was in goal for O's that evening?

1,276. In March 1992 who did O's lose to in a Southern Area semi-final of the Autoglass Trophy by 1–0?

1,277. In January 1993 name the player who made his O's senior debut with a Man of the Match display in the 4–1 win over Wrexham in the second round of the Autoglass Trophy?

1,278. During February 1994 O's lost another Southern area semi-final before 7,010 home fans, who was it against and the score?

1,279. Which London side did O's beat during October 1994 by 5–2 in the Auto Windscreens Shield?

1,280. One of O's favourite sons bagged a hat-trick (one a penalty) that evening, who was he?

1,281. In the Southern area quarter final against Bristol Rovers during January 1995, O's won 4–3 in a penalty shoot-out after a 0–0 draw, who netted O's penalties and who missed one?

1,282. During February and March 1995 who did O's lose to in the Southern Area two-legged Final and what was the aggregate score?

1,283. Over the two-legs what was the total attendance figure?

1,284. In January 1998 name the player who made his senior debut at AFC Bournemouth in the Auto Windscreens Shield?

1,285. Name the player who in December 1998 made his only senior O's appearance in a Auto Windscreen Shield game at Peterborough United?

1,286.   In September 2000 O's went to Newcastle United in the League Cup and lost 2–0, what was the attendance, was it: 7,284, 17,284, 27,284, 37,284 or 47,284?

1,287.   In the second leg O's drew 1–1 with a goal from Stephen Watts, but who was introduced to the 9,522 Brisbane Road crowd for the first time?

1,288.   In the FA Cup during November and December 2000 how many goals did Carl Griffiths score?

1,289.   In the 3–2 after extra-time FA Cup victory over Northwich Victoria on 20 December 2000, who scored O's winner on 116 minutes and how did it come about?

1,290.   In the third round against Tottenham Hotspur on 6 January 2001, which O's lost 0–1, with Carl Griffiths injured in training, which young striker came into the side?

1,291.   In January 2001 name the Australian-born player who made is final senior appearances for O's in an LDV Vans Trophy game at Wycombe Wanderers before returning home after rejecting a contract?

1,292.   In October 2001 O's lost 3–2 by the golden goal rule at Dagenham & Redbridge in the LDV Vans Trophy, who scored that goal and on what time?

1,293.   In January 2002 who did O's win away to in the FA Cup third round and who netted the goals?

1,294.   Even though 35-year-old Iyseden Christie ended as top goalscorer for Tamworth in 2011–12 he was released in May 2012, how many different clubs has he played for during his long career?

1,295.   On 26 January 2002 O's lost in the fourth round at Everton 4–1; what was the attendance, 20,851, 25,851, 35,851 or 45,851?

1,296.   Which player on loan from West Ham United scored in the 3–2 LDV Vans Trophy win against Peterborough United during October 2002?

1,297.   Which Isle of Wight born youth player made a rare start in that same Peterborough match?

1,298.   Which London team did O's knock out of the League Cup during September 2002 and who were O's scorers?

1,299.   Which non-League side knocked O's out of the FA Cup in a replay during November 2002?

1,300.   Where was the replay played?

1,301.   Which non-League side did O's beat away in a first round FA Cup tie during November 2003 and who scored O's goals?

1,302.   Who did O's lose 2–1 to in the LDV Vans Trophy Southern area semi-final during January 2005?

1,303.   Which goalie replaced the injured Glenn Morris in goal in the LDV against Oxford United in November 2005?

1,304.   Which Premier League side did O's knock out of the FA Cup in January 2006 and who scored the goals?

1,304A.   The Johnstone's Paint Trophy comes into being; who scored O's first goal in the 3–1 defeat to Bristol City in November 2006 and on what time was his goal scored?

1,305.   In August 2007 who did O's knock out of the League Cup and who netted O's goals?

1,306.   In September 2007 O's won 1–0 at Notts County in the Johnstone's Paint Trophy Southern Section round one, who scored O's goal and what was significant for the player?

1,307.   On 2 September 2008 O's won 4–2 at Southend United in the JPT, who scored O's goals?

1,308.   Name the youth player who came on in the final minutes of that Southend United game?

1,309.   Who knocked O's out of the FA Cup in a replay during November 2007 after a penalty shoot-out?

1,310.   Who scored the goals that knocked out Bradford City in the FA Cup during November 2008?

1,311.   Who netted the goals in the 2–0 JPT win at Brighton & Hove Albion during September 2010?

1,312.   During October 2010 O's lost another penalty shoot-out at Brentford by 5–4; who missed his spot-kick to send the O's out?

1,313.   What was remarkable about O's FA Cup replay win on Tuesday 7 December 2010?

1,314.   Who scored O's goals and on what time?

1,315.   Whose headed goal at Norwich City earned O's a 1–0 win in the FA Cup third round?

1,316.   In the fourth round which Welsh side did O's beat away on 29 January 2011?

1,317.   Whose goals gave O's a 2–1 win?

1,318.   Whose last minute goal at the Matchroom Stadium secured a replay at the Emirates Stadium against Arsenal in the FA Cup fifth round?

1,319.   O's lost the reply at the Emirates 5–0, but what was the attendance, being the highest ever to watch an O's game; was it 39,361, 49,361, 59,361 or 69,361?

1,319A. How many O's fans bought tickets and attended the Cup game at the Emirates, was it: 5,923, 6,923, 7,923, 8,923, 9,923, or 10,923?

1,320.   In August 2011 O's drew 1–1 at Southend United in the JPT, who scored O's goal?

1,321.   The match saw another penalty shoot-out, with O's winning this time, 4–3; who netted his spot-kick to take O's through?

1,322.   O's had a remarkable penalty shoot-out during September 2011 against Dagenham & Redbridge in the JPT, losing 14–13; who netted O's penalties and who missed O's last kick?

1,323.   Which Premier League side narrowly beat O's in the League Cup losing 3–2 away during September 2011?

1,324.   Which non-League side did O's beat in the first round of the FA Cup during November 2011 and what was the score and who were the goalscorers?

1,325.   Who knocked out O's in round two during December 2011?

1,326. Who scored the most goals for O's in the FA Cup, was it Peter Kitchen, Dennis Pacey, Billy Rees or Barrie Fairbrother?

1,327. What's O's highest ever victory in the FA Cup and who was it against?

1,328. Do you know many FA Cup ties O's have played since entering the competition in 1904 up to and including the defeat by Gillingham in December 2011?

1,329. How many FA Cup victories have been recorded by O's?

1,329A. List the full playing record of O's in the League Cup 1960 to 2011–12?

1,330. Do you think O's have scored more FA Cup goals than they have conceded?

Answers

Answers for Chapter 1

1.	Nathan or Natie, if my wife is angry at me.
1A.	1881
2.	Old boys from Homerton College, a teacher training college for non-conformists and Puritans.
3.	Cricket
4.	Eagle
5.	Mr Rene Gronland
6.	3 March 1888
7.	The commencement of the Football League.
8.	The name was suggested by Jack R. Dearing who worked for the Orient Steamship Navigation Company; he was involved in the launch of their ship the SS Orient in 1879.
9.	Red shirts, with a large white 'O' on their back and white shorts.
10.	The supporters would shout out 'Play up or Buck up the O's' and the name stuck.
11.	Glyn Road, Hackney
12.	Clapton & District League
13.	June 1898
14.	Winning their first Cup, the West Ham Charity Cup, beating Clapton FC, 1–0.
15.	Jack Hilsdon
16.	Millwall
17.	November 1903
18.	11–0 (goals from Wallace 4, McGeorge 3, Jones 2, Bush 1 and Seeley 1)
19.	Brighton & Hove Albion, a 0–0 draw
20.	Two players missed the train; with only nine players on the field, O's lost 13–0.
21.	Samuel Ormerod

Answers to Chapter 2

22.   Horatio William Bottomley

23.   Manchester

24.   Peter Boyle

25.   £4

26.   Herbert Kingaby with a header on 62 minutes at Leicester Fosse on 2 September 1905, O's lost 2–1.

27.   He took Aston Villa to court in 1906 claiming he was denied freedom of movement to another club. The case, which he lost, lasted until March 1912. It was the Players Union who paid all his costs of £725 and Kingaby was classed as an amateur for the remainder of his career.

28.   O's beat Glossop North End 2–0 on 11 September 1905, with two goals from Walter Leigh.

29.   Peter Proudfoot

30.   Harold Halse

31.   Walter Leigh, all four

32.   18,046 at West Bromwich Albion on 25 December 1905.

33.   Bottom on 21 points

34.   O's obtained 21 votes, one more than Oldham Athletic, so remained in League Division Two and Oldham had to wait for another year.

Answers to Chapter 3

35.   Billy Martin

36.   He was totally bald and being a very sensitive fellow, he wore a skull-cap on the field, and wig off it.

37.   Anthony Michael Leonard in the 3–0 win against Glossop North End.

38.   Spider, he went on to play 11 seasons for O's and was the first player to make over 300 League appearances.

39.   They wore new kit, white shirts with a red chevron on the front and back, and black shorts; they wore the same kit at home until 1931.

40. Baseball, O's beat Fulham 8–7 in the final of the British Baseball Association Cup in 1907, the star player being Mickey Leonard, who also played for the British-born players versus the American-born players. Two years later O's beat Leyton 6–5 in the final and were crowned champions for the second time.

41. 26,000

42. 3–2, with goals from Fred Parker (2) and Toby Underwood.

43. Dix never told Portsmouth he was leaving them to join O's, they complained to the Football League and O's were ordered to pay Pompey £100 for the player.

44. 4th

45. O's beat Millwall 3–0 (Parker, Scott & Prior) to win the Dubonnet Cup before 12,000 French fans at the Parc Des Princes Stadium. The Cup is now housed in the British Museum.

46. Richard McFadden

47. Woolwich Arsenal

48. O's were unbeaten, P14 D5 L0

49. Ike van den Eynden, he made 12 League appearances.

50. The Gunners missed out on promotion on goal difference over Bradford Park Avenue. A win would have seen them promoted.

51. William 'Billy' Bower, the goalkeeper made 176 League and Cup appearances between 1905 and 1915.

52. It was the final match before the players went off to war and the highlights of the match and the players parading around the pitch in their uniforms after the game was captured on Pathe News.

Answers Chapter 4

53. 40, the highest number from any other League club in the country.

54. William Jonas, Richard McFadden and George Scott. Gone, but Never Forgotten.

55. John William Mew
56. Santander FC, Royal Betis and Barcelona, in Spain; he died a forgotten man in London during 1959.
57. He tore up his notes and refused to send his report to the editor.
58. James Dimmock with seven goals
59. 18
60. Arthur Layton

Answers to Chapter 5

61. James, John 'Jack' and Samuel Tonner
62. 12 League games and 1 FA Cup tie
63. Robert 'Bob' Spottiswood
64. Crystal Palace
65. The Prince of Wales and the Duke of York
66. William Marsden Holmes, he had been with the club, both as a player and manager for just over 16 years.
67. John and Robert Duffus and Jack and Sam Tonner
68. Owen and Thomas Williams
69. He is the first O's player to win a full England cap, against Ireland, played at West Bromwich on 21 October 1922, he won one further cap against Wales on 5 March 1923.
70. United put in a £2,500 offer for the player while he was sitting in the visitors' dressing room at Old Trafford with his O's teammates. He signed, said his farewells, changed dressing rooms, and scored against O's in United's 4–2 victory.
71. Bertram Leonard Rosier, from the penalty spot.
72. Clatworthy
73. Donald James Cock with 13 League and 3 FA Cup goals.
74. John George Leather, it was the amateur player's only League game, O's lost 6–0.
75. Sir Hubert Ashton, he made five League appearances in the 1926–27 season.
76. O's won 5–1

Answers

77.   Leslie Ethelbert George Ames, he made 14 appearances for
        O's down the right wing during his stay and played 49 Tests
        for England, scored 32,248 career runs, with 703 catches
        and 418 stumpings.
78.   Herbert George Batten
79.   Rutherford, a real legend in his own time with both
        Newcastle United and Arsenal; he was aged 42 years and
        172 days, making him the oldest player to appear for O's,
        until 47-year-old Peter Shilton played in 1996.
80.   Donald Cock with 15 League goals and Robert Dennison
        with 13 League and 2 FA Cup goals.
81.   O's conceded 102 goals (96 in the League and 6 in the FA
        Cup), the most ever in one season.
82.   O's staged an international boxing tournament before
        32,000 fans, including the Prince of Wales. The main event
        saw Johnny Hill beat American David 'Newsboy' Brown
        over 15 rounds to take the vacant World Flyweight title, to
        become the first Scotsman to hold a World title and the
        sound of *Loch Lomond* could be heard for miles all around
        Clapton. Also on the bill was Cockney favourite Teddy
        Baldock who won inside two rounds over American Johnny
        Brown when the towel came into the ring.
83.   O's lost 3–2 before a record Millfields Road attendance of
        37,615 spectators.
84.   Relegated for the first time in their history ending bottom of
        Division Town with 32 points.
85.   They lost at home to Plymouth Argyle 2–0 before 18,054
        fans.
86.   O's won three of their last four games: beating Luton Town
        6–1, Bristol Rovers 3–0, lost at Bournemouth 5–1 and they
        beat Brighton 4–1.
87.   Brighton & Hove Albion, winning 4–1 before 8,763 fans on
        3 May 1930.
88.   30 years

Answers to Chapter 6

89. Lea Bridge Road

90. John 'Jack' Fowler with five goals from the first three games.

91. O's were forced to close the ground for changes to be made and play three games elsewhere.

92. Two League games were played at Wembley Stadium, beating Brentford 3–0 on 22 November 1930 and on 6 December 1930, a 3–1 win over Southend United. An FA Cup tie against Luton Town was also played at Highbury, O's losing 2–4.

93. Brentford, 8,319 and Southend United 1,916 (on a wet and windy Saturday).

94. Reginald Tricker, with four goals from the final five games, ending with 20 League and FA Cup goals for the season from 31 appearances.

95. Thames

96. Arthur Cropper against Torquay United on 14 March 1931.

97. James Marshall Seed

98. £14 per week

99. 373 League and 22 FA Cup appearances, including a record 225 consecutive appearances between September 1921 and May 1931.

100. Herbert John Emery

101. Charles Fletcher, 22 goals (20 League and 2 FA Cup goals).

102. Being the shortest footballer to play in the Football League, standing at just 5ft 0in.

103. George Raymond Phillips and Wilfred John Phillips (not related).

104. David Imrie, making 12 League appearances with 7 goals.

105. Thomas James Frederick Mills

106. He was knocked down by a lorry on 15 May 1979 and died from his injuries, aged 67.

107. O's won 9–1 on 10 February 1934 (Halliday 3, Ware 2, Mayson, Mills, Rigby and Crawford).

108. He netted 19 goals from 22 League and FA Cup appearances that season and a total of 36 goals from 56 appearances during a two-year spell.
109. Left-back Wynn Crompton and left-half Edward Alfred George Ware.
110. Scottish born 24-year-old left winger James Bow, in a 3–1 home defeat to non-League Chester.
111. Edmund Charles Crawford with 23 League and 2 FA Cup goals.
112. 20,288 fans, however, police reported that at least 1,000 Millwall fans had broken into the ground without paying, to swell the numbers to over 21,300.
113. With Swindon Town, Newport County and O's all finishing on 29 points, O's were saved by having a slightly better goal difference, in the end both Swindon and Newport were re-elected for the following season.
114. They owed the Football League and other creditors £2,000.
115. Charlton Athletic
116. The Godfrey Phillips Company in Hackney gave O's £400, the Supporters' Club raised £50, the Gliksten brothers, owners of Charlton Athletic gave £40, and a cheque from the Prince of Wales for £2,000 all helped to save the club.
117. Frank Snewin
118. Thomas Lucas, 37 years old
119. David Hyman Morris, the Jewish player netted a career total of 290 League goals from 421 appearances (O's career 13 appearances with 8 League goals).
120. David Halliday 3 and Arthur Rigby 2 goals.
121. David Halliday
122. Willie Boyd became the first player to score 5 League goals against O's.
123. Harold and Jack Smith and Harold and John Taylor, neither were related.
124. Edmund Charles Crawford
125. Seven years, 1930 to 1937

126. Southend United on a Thursday afternoon 29 April 1937, O's won 3–0.
127. 2,541
128. Due to injuries, Rossiter, a full-back, played at centre-forward.
129. He broke his leg, ending his playing career.
130. Brisbane Road, in Leyton
131. Leyton FC
132. Cardiff City, 1–1
133. 14,598
134. Frederick Charles Arnold Tully
135. No, Woolwich Arsenal faced Leicester Fosse at the Leyton Cricket Ground on 9 March 1895.
136. The name remained as Clapton Orient
137. Charles Alfred Fletcher, in a 3–0 win over Bournemouth & Boscombe Athletic on 9 September 1937.
138. 19,896, against Millwall on 23 October 1937, O's won 2–1.
139. Oliver Eustace Tidman
140. 5–0, O's ending two points clear of both Bristol Rovers and Walsall.
141. An own-goal from Vale's Jonathan 'Jonty' Rowe.
142. Roderick Williams, 18 League and Cup goals.
143. Tom Halsey
144. Frederick Hanley joined from Chelsea in July 1939.
145. It was abandoned after just three League games, due to the outbreak of World War Two.
146. Ipswich Town, Southend United and Watford
147. Ipswich (Home) 2–2, Southend (Home) 0–0 and Watford (Away) 1–1.
148. Leonard Victor Allum (1 app), John Ellis (3 apps), Leslie Hann (2 apps), William McFadyen (3 apps) and John Law McNeill 3 apps).
149. He let in 12 goals on 13 April 1936 against Luton Town, with Joe Payne bagging 10 of them.
150. In season 1931–32 he netted 52 goals from 38 Scottish League appearances.

Answers to Chapter 7

150A.   Robert Shankly
151.   James Sperrin, O's lost 9–0
152.   David Jack Levene
153.   15–2
154.   Leslie Compton, normally a defender he turned out at centre-forward that day due to players being away on National Service. He made 253 League appearances for them and only managed five goals.
155.   Jack Rawlings, making six appearances for O's with one goal in 1940–41.
156.   Frank Butterworth
157.   115 goals, with 19 defeats and one draw (3–3 with Arsenal).
158.   Frank Charles Shufflebottom
159.   Jack Thorogood
160.   Walter Reginald O'Dell
161.   William Henry Strauss, who made his appearances for O's in 1941–42.
162.   John Joseph Hewitt, he made 39 appearances, scoring 14 goals.
163.   16–1, Pompey forward Andy Black netting eight of the goals.
164.   John Hewitt against Fulham on 21 November 1942, O's won 4–2 before 2,995 fans.
165.   Ernest Muttitt
166.   James Sime McLuckie, with 21 wartime appearances and one goal between 1942 and 1944.
167.   George Hedley Swindin
168.   Trevor Ford
169.   John Gilbert Hay Liddell
170.   Les Gore and Alec Stock
171.   Fred Bartlett with 207 appearances.
172.   Frederick William Dawes 1939–40 and Albert George Dawes in 1944–45.

173. The Aberdeen hotshot Matthew Armstrong with 26 goals from 41 appearances between 1941 and 1943.
174. Howard Francis John Rickett
175. Alexander Younger
176. Albert Robson, making seven wartime appearances and six goals for O's in 1944–45.
177. John Dugnolle
178. George William 'Willie' Hall
179. He was struck down with Thrombosis and eventually had both legs amputated.

Answers to Chapter 8

180. 30
181. Charles William Hewitt
182. White shirts with a blue chevron and black shorts.
183. Ipswich Town, 2–2 before 12,530 fans
184. George James Willshaw and William Charles Brown.
185. He changed his surname to Armitage, all his first-team appearances for O's were under his previous surname.
186. He wanted to sign a new player, and was told that funds were not available, so he walked out.
187. The former Bolton Wanderers and Reading player and FC Rouen of France and Crystal Palace coach, William Bulloch Wright.
188. 19 days
189. He lost all three matches that he was in charge, at Reading (21 September) 0–2, Crystal Palace at home (28 September) 0–1 and at Torquay United (5 October) 2–3.
190. The directors persuaded Charles Hewitt to return and Wright reverted to his duties as coach.
191. Robert Rollo Jack, he was with O's as a player between 1929 and 1932 making 83 senior appearances with 22 goals.
192. The club officially changed its name to Leyton Orient Football Club, after 48 years as Clapton Orient.

193.   O's won 3–1

194.   Raymond King

195.   He broke his wrist.

196.   King joined Port Vale and made 275 senior appearances, including playing in an FA Cup quarter-final against O's, which they win 1–0 before 31,000 Brisbane Road fans.

197.   Cyril William Bacon, a wing-half with 40 appearances.

198.   Bacon scored two goals.

199.   William Ian Brown, known as Billy 'Buster' Brown.

200.   37 years and three months

201.   It was the first time an O's Football League match was played in June, this due to the continued inclement weather.

202.   Douglas Arthur Hunt with 14 goals (13 League and 1 FA Cup).

203.   Fourth from bottom on 32 points.

204.   Arthur Edward Page

205.   Royal blue shirts with white shorts

206.   Ronald Duncan Sales, with a penalty against Crystal Palace on 23 August 1947.

207.   Stanley Albert Tolliday

208.   Harold Frank Neary

209.   Frederick Leslie Bartlett

210.   24,864

211.   He netted six goals in the final four games, helping O's to three wins and one draw.

212.   Neil McBain

213.   He played in goal due to injuries in a Football League match for New Brighton aged 52 years and 4 months, making him the oldest player ever to appear in the League.

214.   Sixth from bottom on 36 points, with the bottom three teams all on 34 points.

215.   Left-back, Ledger Ritson and inside-forward, William James Alfred Stroud.

216.   Ted Crawford's, 23 goals in 1935–36

217.   Archie McFeat of Torquay United on 20 November 1948.

218.   Inflicted O's heaviest League defeat, 7–1, on 16 April 1949.

219. O's 1,338th League match.
220. Polish born, Stanislaw Eugeniusz Gerula.
221. The 1952 FA Amateur Cup Final for Walthamstow Avenue in their 2–1 defeat of Leyton.
222. 17 times
223. Frank Neary's 25 League goals, a new O's record.
224. Harry Zussman
225. Alec Stock as manager, he was player-manager with Yeovil.
226. He was 32 years of age, making him the youngest manager in the Football League at the time.
227. He became the first player to score a hat-trick against the same team both home and away in the same season.
228. Ipswich Town, a 4–4 draw at Portman Road during September 1949 and a 4–0 home win during January 1950.
229. Queen's Park Rangers
230. Oliver Henry Lucas
231. St Mirren
232. Away at Notts County in October 1949 by 7–1
233. Roy Patrick Welton
234. 36,436

Answers to Chapter 9

235. Aldershot
236. Centre-forward Charlie Mortimer scored five goals, only the second player to do so against O's in the Football League.
237. Sidney George Hobbins
238. With 10 seconds left, O's were down 2–1, the ball was hoofed up into the Southend penalty area and Wally Pullen with his back to goal, flicked the ball backwards and into the net, for a 2–2 draw and O's were saved and the Shrimpers lost a bit of money.
239. Newport County, Aldershot and Walsall.
240. William Derek Rees for £14,500.
241. James Alfred Blair with 16 League goals from 45 appearances.

242.   Goalkeeper, Pat Welton, with 46 League appearances and 1 FA Cup appearance.

243.   James Leonard Lewis

244.   O's beat Torquay United 5–1 on 10 March 1951.

245.   36-year-old Gilbert Swinburne Glidden, it was his only League game for O's.

246.   Billy Rees with 11 goals, 10 League and 1 in the FA Cup.

246A.   Jack Tonner

247.   Robert Bruce

248.   One, a 1–0 defeat at Bristol Rovers on 27 February 1952.

249.   O's beat Colchester United 7–0 on 5 January 1952.

250.   Dennis Pacey 2, Tommy Harris 2, Tommy Brown 1, Billy Rees 1 and Paddy Blatchford 1.

251.   Pacey with 17 goals, 11 in the League and 6 in the FA Cup.

252.   Brian Harvill Jackson

253.   £7,500 plus winger Donald Woan.

254.   2,032

255.   O's won 4–2

256.   Stanley Elvey Reginald Aldous with 55 appearances.

257.   After a very cold spell, resulting in more coal usage in homes, this caused a thick layer of smog that hung over the capital resulting in over 4,000 deaths.

258.   Ken Facey and Dennis Pacey bagged two each.

259.   He netted four goals in O's 5–3 win over Colchester United.

260.   He scored 19 League goals.

261.   Both David Groombridge and Patrick Welton made 23 appearances each.

262.   0

263.   42 points

264.   Joseph Mallett

265.   Michael Rupert Burgess

266.   17,306 against Ipswich Town on 16 January 1954.

267.   Three own-goals, scored by Johnstone of Swindon Town, Bowler of Millwall and Harrison of Colchester United.

268.   George Henry Poulton

269. Four, against Bournemouth, Walsall, Crystal Palace and Tranmere Rovers.

270. John Richard Smith. Queen's Park Rangers at the age of 20.

271. John Hartburn

272. Roy Kirk, the Coventry wing-half scored two own-goals.

273. 7–1

274. Victor George Groves

275. It's O's record away League win.

276. 31 goals

277. Alfred Stanley Morgan

278. Six

279. Three, all at home against Colchester United, Workington (FA Cup) and Norwich City.

280. In second place on 61 points.

281. 89 League and 3 FA Cup goals = 92 goals

282. It was the highest number, up to that point, scored by O's in a League season.

283. Bristol City on 70 points.

284. Philip Abraham Woosnam

285. Benjamin Robert Vincent Fenton

286. If you have a good memory, yes, the same player from question 272, Roy Kirk.

287. Both Stan Charlton and Vic Groves had been sold to Arsenal.

288. £30,000

289. The attendance dropped by over 10,000 fans.

290. 8–0

291. It was the first time O's had scored eight goals and they also won the match by a record margin (they had scored nine goals in February 1934, but that was by 9–2).

292. Leonard Bruce Julians

293. Walthamstow Avenue

294. Thomas Bourhill Johnston from Newport County

295. £5,500 plus O's forward Mike Burgess

296. £2,000

297.   Harry Zussman
298.   Skipper Stan Aldous
299.   Newport Station
300.   It was Frederick Leslie Gore.
301.   Having turned down the manager's job at Middlesbrough, he was appointed assistant manager to Tom Whittaker at Arsenal.
302.   53 days before returning to O's.
303.   'My mind said Arsenal, my heart said Orient'
304.   John Hartburn 4 and Ronald Heckman 3
305.   Johnston 3, Heckman 2, Woosnam 2 and Hartburn 1
306.   21 goals
307.   Millwall
308.   2–1, with goals from Hartburn and Johnston.
309.   It was scored direct from a corner-kick.
310.   They scored 106 League goals.
311.   Ron Heckman scored 29 League and FA Cup goals and John Hartburn scored 23 League and FA Cup goals.
312.   The first time
313.   O's made a profit of £17,965 and the average League home attendance that season was 17,597.
314.   David James Sexton
315.   West Ham United for £2,000
316.   4–3
317.   O's lost 7–1
318.   Reuben Cook
319.   Three, Dave Groombridge (24 apps), Pat Welton (17 apps), and Frank George (1 app).
320.   15th
321.   They lost 7–2 at Grimsby Town.
322.   Les Gore
323.   Phil McKnight and Phil Woosnam
324.   James Harold Smith
325.   37 League apps with 3 goals and 2 apps in the FA Cup.
326.   Staged a Testimonial match for him against an All Star X1 on 24 September 1958.

327. Bradford City, O's won 3–2 with goals from Sid Bishop, Len Julians and Phil White.
328. He scored 35 League goals from 30 appearances.
329. He signed for Blackburn Rovers for £15,000.
330. He scored 43 goals, 35 for Orient and 8 goals for Rovers, making him the top League goalscorer in the country.
331. None (he only played once in the FA Cup).
332. Alec Stock returned as manager after an eight month spell in Italy with AS Roma.
333. 51 goals, Johnston with his 35 goals and Len Julians with 16 League goals.
334. The London five-a-side championship.
335. Millwall 1–0, Tottenham Hotspur 3–1, Queen's Park Rangers 1–0 and Crystal Palace in the Final 1–0.
336. Groombridge, Lea, Woosnam, Julians and Andrews
337. Patrick Joseph Hasty with two goals and Mark Lazarus with one goal.
338. Paddy
339. He joined Arsenal for £12,000.
340. Joseph Patrick Elwood against Bristol City on 29 November.
341. Phil Woosnam
342. £30,000
343. Helping to set up professional soccer in America.
344. Edwin 'Eddy' Brown from Birmingham City.
345. A first-team friendly against Queen's Park Rangers on 24 January, O's won 9–1, he netted a hat-trick.
346. Both teams had a spare Saturday due to previously being knocked out of the FA Cup.
347. Tommy Johnston from Blackburn Rovers
348. Sunderland 6–0 on 30 March and Charlton Athletic 6–1 on 11 April.
349. Brown 5, Elwood 3, and Baily, Facey, Johnston and White 1 each.
350. 'The Cheeky Chappie'
351. Brown, Elwood and Johnston, all ended on 10 goals each.
352. Les Gore
353. Terence James McDonald against Hull City in a 3–1 victory.

354.	John Sewell
355.	Joseph Elwood, in a 1–1 draw at Portsmouth on 28 December 1959.

Answers to Chapter 10

356.	Anthony Biggs
357.	Pat Boone
358.	A hat, on his return to America, he sent each player a hat.
359.	He missed one penalty, in a 4–1 win over Ipswich Town during August 1959.
360.	It was Brown's 200th career League goal and Johnston's 25th League goal of the season.
361.	Don Gibson
362.	Thomas Richard Donald Gibson
363.	It was the first match at Brisbane Road played under floodlights.
364.	O's won 2–1 with goals from Sid Bishop and a Ken Facey penalty before 12,937 fans.
365.	£15,500
366.	David Henry Groombridge
367.	133 League and 9 FA Cup appearances between 1951 and 1960.
368.	William Gibb Robertson
369.	Chelsea for £1,000
370.	Trefor Owen
371.	Errol Gilmour Crossan
372.	22,131 at Liverpool on 11 February 1961.
373.	O's lost 5–0
374.	Dave Hickson
375.	Alan William Sealey
376.	Standing with his back towards the goal he back-heeled the ball into the net to secure a 2–1 win against Luton Town.
377.	David Gerald Ivor Dunmore
378.	No manager was in charge at the time, the deal was signed by the Hammers chairman Reg Pratt.

379. Andrew Thomas Smillie, but he refused to move.
380. O's won 1–0
381. Tommy Johnston
382. It was his last League goal for the club.
383. 121 League goals from 180 appearances and two FA Cup goals from seven appearances.
384. Goalkeeper Albert Cochran and full-back William Taylor.
385. Johnston spotted him when on a coaching mission for O's in Scotland playing for Bonnyrigg Rose and recommended him to the club.
386. Tommy Johnston with 46 League and Cup appearances.
387. Kenneth William Facey, he coached the youth and reserve sides.
388. 301 League appearances with 74 goals, 19 FA Cup appearances with five goals and three League Cup appearances with no goals.
389. Second, behind Tommy Johnston.
390. He converted 23 penalties and missed four until being overtaken over in later years by Matthew Lockwood.
391. John Joseph Carey
392. Les Gore and Eddie Baily
393. O's won 5–1
394. Malcolm Graham with a hat-trick, David Dunmore and Ronald Foster, one each.
395. Norman Victor Deeley from Wolverhampton Wanderers for £12,000.
396. He scored direct from a corner-kick.
397. Gordon Edward Bolland from Chelsea for £9,000.
398. The money was paid personally by both chairman Harry Zussman and director Leslie Grade.
399. 3–3
400. David Dunmore
401. David George Clark
402. Derek Gibbs, who netted twice.
403. Ron Baynham
404. O's won 2–0

405.	They could only draw 1–1.
406.	Malcolm Graham
407.	Ronnie Foster
408.	21,617
409.	Their transistor radios
410.	Liverpool were crowned champions of Division Two.
411.	Yes
412.	None
413.	O's lost 2–1 to Arsenal
414.	26,300
415.	Derek Gibbs
416.	West Ham United
417.	2–0 with goals from David Dunmore and Malcolm Graham.
418.	51,542, it's the highest total to watch an O's League match.
419.	Manchester United 1–0 and Everton 3–0.
420.	Terry McDonald with a wonder strike in the final minute of the game.
421.	Norman Deeley, Gordon Bolland and David Dunmore.
422.	Manchester United, 24,901, and Everton 21,756.
423.	Michael John Pinner
424.	30,987
425.	19-year-old Gordon Harold Gregory
426.	He scored
427.	Harry
428.	Malcolm Musgrove for £11,000.
429.	He scored with his very first kick.
430.	19 games
431.	Away at Bolton Wanderers 1–0 on 15 April 1963.
432.	Robert Henry Mason, he joined from Wolverhampton Wanderers.
433.	Chelmsford City from the Southern League Premier Division.
434.	£20,000
435.	No goals
436.	Liverpool by 2–1
437.	Centre-half Sid Bishop with a grand long distance kick, being his only goal of the season.

438. 21 points
439. 'Leslie, may I be honest with you, please don't waste your money.'
440. 16,406
441. David Dunmore with 14 goals (11 League, 1 FA Cup and 2 in the League Cup) and also Malcolm Graham with 14 goals (9 League, 0 FA Cup and 5 in the League Cup).
442. Yes, Stanley Charlton with 42 League, 4 FA Cup and 5 League Cup appearances = 51 appearances.
443. Nottingham Forest
444. Yes, loyal servant, Les Gore.
445. Gerald Ward for £8,000
446. Ronald Saunders
447. O's lost 6–3 at home on 26 October 1963 and 4–3 away on 7 March 1964.
448. Stanley Charlton
449. Edward Lewis
450. Benjamin Robert Vincent Fenton
451. Gordon Bolland for £31,000
452. The legendary veteran Ipswich Town forward Edward John Phillips for £8,000.
453. The Panthers and The Soundcasters.
454. Cardiff City, 4–0
455. Mel and John Charles and Ivor Allchurch.
456. Philip George John White
457. White made between 1953 and 1964, 217 League appearances with 28 goals and 16 Cup appearances with 0 goals.
458. O's beat Portsmouth 5–2
459. Ted Phillips
460. Terence Edmund Price
461. David James Webb
462. They lost 6–0 at Manchester City
463. O's beat Manchester City 4–3 with two goals each from Dunmore and Phillips.
464. O's won 5–2, with goals from Terry McDonald 2, Ted Phillips 2 and Terry Price 1.

465. He picked up the ball on the halfway line and hammered the ball into the net.
466. Les Gore
467. He signed David Metchick from Fulham and he scored on debut against Charlton Athletic on a snow covered pitch.
468. Thomas Joseph Dunne
469. They picked up four draws.
470. David James Sexton
471. Peter Charles Allen
472. Adrian Ernest Thorne
473. 19-year old, James Dennis Scott
474. Colin Harold Flatt
475. Paul Frank Went aged 15 years and 327 days.
476. Reuben Noble-Lazarus for Barnsley as a playing sub against Ipswich Town in 2008 aged 15 years and 45 days.
477. Joseph Elwood replaced the injured Jimmy McGeorge.
478. Sturdily built, John Smith hit a 25–yard beauty against Bolton Wanderers for the two points.
479. He resigned.
480. Richard Peter Le Flem
481. Bradford-on-Avon, Wiltshire
482. David Metchick
482A. Dennis James Sorrell and Colin Harvey Worrell.
483. Thomas Ernest Jenkins
484. They gained two rare draws, Manchester City 2–2 and Southampton 1–1.
485. 19,839
486. 23 points, 10 points behind second from bottom Middlesbrough.
487. Richard Douglas Graham
488. He signed Terry Bradbury from Southend United in exchange for Colin Flatt in June 1966.
489. He swapped Harry Gregory for Charlton Athletic veteran, 38-year-old Clifford Holton and also defender John Snedden.
490. He signed 30-year-old Brian Whitehouse for £10,000.

491.   Gore, Holton and Whitehouse

492.   All blue

493.   George O'Brien

494.   3–1 against Scunthorpe United on 27 August 1966.

495.   Price, Metchick and Whitehouse

496.   Kenneth Robert Woodward at Bournemouth on 24 September 1966, O's lost 1–0.

497.   Edwin Werge

498.   The famous 'Pass the Bucket' meeting where money was raised to save the club from closure.

499.   Barry Francis Fry

500.   They won 3–1, only their third away victory all season.

501.   Defender John Snedden, playing at centre-forward for the first time in his career.

502.   Michael Keith Jones in a 4–1 win over Doncaster Rovers on 15 April 1967.

503.   Cliff Holton with 17 League goals.

504.   The club changed their name to Orient Football Club and their colours to an all red strip with a thin white stripe down the shorts.

505.   Leyton had been merged into the new Waltham Forest Borough.

506.   John Still and Tommy Taylor.

507.   15 years and 334 days, making him the second youngest player to play for O's first team behind Paul Went.

508.   The match against Torquay was his only League appearance for O's.

509.   1 goal, a penalty against Gillingham in the League Cup on 22 August 1967.

510.   He had to retire due to a vein problem in his leg.

511.   294 League goals from 570 appearances during his 20 years in the game.

512.   Terence John Mancini

513.   Roy Massey with 13 League and Cup goals.

514.   Youth coach at Arsenal.

515.   The board would not give him any money for new players,

so for the match at Watford on the 24th, he was forced to play a youngster who was already injured and he felt guilty.

516. Graham Leonard Archell, the story being confirmed by Archell from his home in Perth, Australia.

517. Peter Frank Angell for one League match at Southport, a 0–0 draw.

518. James Henry Bloomfield

519. John Henry Arnott, O's won away 3–2

520. Winger, John Peter Key

521. Roy Massey with 12 goals

522. Peter Brabrook for £10,000

523. Stephen John Bowtell

524. 8

525. Keith Simpson introduced Herb Alpert and the Tijuana Brass' song *Tijuana Taxi*, sadly Simpson died in October 2002, the song has been played as players come out onto the field for over 40 years.

526. 1946–47, the players ran out to a military march composed by Czech composer Julius Fačík called *Entrance of the Gladiators*.

527. Victor Lewis Halom for £35,000.

528. Michael Edwin Bullock from Oxford United during October for £10,000 and John Barry Dyson from Watford during December for £8,000.

529. O's beat Shrewsbury Town by 4–0 with goals from Bullock, Dyson, Mancini and Harper.

530. 7 League goals (including 2 penalties).

531. Barry Dyson with 10 League goals.

532. He retired from playing to concentrate on his managerial duties.

533. None

534. Barrie Edward Fairbrother in the 1–0 win over Mansfield Town.

535. 18,861

536. Mark Lazarus

Answers to Chapter 11

537.   Top of Division Three, ahead of Luton Town
538.   Mark Lazarus against Shrewsbury Town, in the 1–0 win on 25 April 1970.
539.   Mickey Bullock with 19 goals.
540.   16 players
541.   4 players
542.   Mick Jones, Tommy Taylor, Peter Allen and Barry Dyson
543.   Roma of Italy, O's lost 3–1 before 8,300 fans.
544.   Third Division Manager of the Year
545.   Mark Lazarus scored twice and he celebrated each time with his usual lap of honour all around the pitch.
546.   Because of torrential heavy rain.
547.   Robert Moss
548.   Paul Edwin Harris
549.   Chiropodist
550.   29 goals
551.   It was the lowest number of League goals scored by an O's team in a season since entry into the Football League back in 1905.
552.   Mark Lazarus with 6 goals
553.   Alice Underwood, sadly Alice died in Whipps Cross Hospital on 23 December 1987.
554.   Ian Bowyer for £25,000
555.   First Division side Leicester City
556.   £6,000
557.   Chairman Arthur Page was on holiday in Spain and his Deputy Neville Ovenden accepted the compensation; on his return Page was so angry that Ovenden resigned from the board.
558.   George William Petchey
559.   John Falltrick
560.   A hat-trick against Cardiff City on 21 August 1971.
561.   Philip Frederick William Hoadley from Crystal Palace for £30,000.
562.   O's lost 5–3

563.	Arthur Sydney Rowe

564.	O's won 5–0 with goals from Bullock (2), Walley and Bowyer (2).

565.	O's were playing Birmingham City in second place who had to win to gain promotion over their nearest rivals Millwall, so the crowd was swelled by big numbers of both Birmingham and Millwall fans. Birmingham won 1–0 and were promoted over Millwall.

566.	Ian Bowyer with 17 League and Cup goals.

567.	Dennis Rofe joined Leicester City for a record fee for a full-back at the time of £112,000.

568.	Gerald Queen for a reported £50,000

569.	He has been one of the top youth soccer coaches in Florida

570.	Richard Alfred Heppolette for £43,000.

571.	Bhusawal, Bombay, India on 8 April 1949.

572.	O's won seven games on the trot, scoring 19 goals.

573.	Barrie Fairbrother with 11 League goals.

574.	Peter Barnes

575.	Ernest Shepherd, who acted as O's coach, physio and assistant manager, he stayed until 1976.

576.	O's won 3–0 with goals from Bullock (2) and Queen.

577.	Michael John O'Shaughnessy

578.	A Stuart Pearson penalty.

579.	O's won 4–2 with goals from Queen (2), Bullock and Fairbrother.

580.	He injured his back, and had to miss quite a number of games, on his return he was never quite the same player.

581.	David Payne for £20,000, John Keith Jackson for £30,000 and William Robert Roffey for £5,000.

582.	O's beat Crystal Palace 3–0 with goals from Bullock and Fairbrother (2)

583.	Carlisle United, O's lost 3–0 and we got back home late, so missing the highlights, thank goodness, as shown on BBC Match of the Day that evening.

584.	Oxford United, a 1–1 draw on 10 March, with Derek Downing scoring O's goal with a low headed goal.

585. O's could only draw 1–1 before 29,766 fans and so O's missed out on promotion by a single point.
586. 11,793
587. Barrie Fairbrother
588. Derek James Possee for £60,000.
589. 5ft 5in
590. Manchester United, O's lost at home 2–0.
591. Laurence Paul Cunningham, O's beat Oldham Athletic 3–1.
592. John Thomas Walley
593. Laurie Cunningham
593A. A heavy fine, he arrived late for the pre-match talk and was told by manager Petchey that unless he scored he would be heavily fined.
594. 12
595. 28 goals
596. Possee, with 7 goals from 34(1) League appearances.
597. 39 League goals
598. O's beat Queens Park Rangers 6–1 in the Final of the London 5-a-side Championship, to win the tournament for the second time.
599. Charlie Hasler, he stayed for 25 years.
600. He swopped both Terry Brisley and Barrie Fairbrother for Millwall's Douglas Stewart Allder.
601. No goals from 19(4) League appearances.
602. Malcolm Beason, Nigel Gray, Mike Everitt and Gary Hibbs.
603. Left winger, Roy William Cotton
604. Laurie Cunningham with eight League goals.
605. O's beat Tottenham Hotspur 2–0 in the final of the National Five-a-side Championships at the Wembley indoor arena.
606. Laurie Cunningham
607. George Petchey
608. Derek Clarke from Oxford United for £10,000.
609. Defender Phil Hoadley scored twice in the 2–2 home draw with Plymouth Argyle on 4 September 1976.
610. Alan Whittle
611. A new club badge

612.   Two Wyverns, facing each other are the main features of the crest.

613.   A football and 1881, as the year of the club's foundation.

614.   Clive M. Brown, Mark Hodges and finished off by club chairman Brian Bernard Winston.

615.   Four worn on the shirts and one on the club programme.

616.   1. 28 Sept 1946 to 1965, the arms of the Borough of Leyton. With the Latin motto Ministrando Dignitas meaning 'Dignity through service', in later years the Latin motto was replaced by the club name.
        2. August 1965 to December 1966, a small badge designed by manager Dave Sexton of blue and white stripes were worn.
        3. August 1966 to an oval badge worn on the shirts with the colours of the P&O shipping group of blue, white and yellow on the suggestion of director Reg Briggs, who was involved in shipping. However, on the club programme they had another badge that of a single wyvern.
        4. On 15 August 1971 O's introduced a left facing motif on their shirts of a griffin, a mythical creature which guarded against all and kept evil spirits away.

617.   Laurie Cunningham for £135,000, and two Albion players.

618.   Allan Richard Glover and Joseph Mayo.

619.   Fulham, O's were down 6–0 at half-time and won the second half 1–0 (as the O's fans would tell their Fulham counterparts at the match), O's losing 6–1.

620.   John Mitchell with 4 goals.

621.   Allan Glover in a 1–1 draw.

622.   Goalie John Jackson fumbled the ball into his own net, but O's held on for survival in Division Two.

623.   Arthur Edward Page

624.   George Petchey

625.   £45,000

626.   Chairman Brian Winston sacked Petchey.

627.   Bob Hatton, scored inside five minutes.

628.	Peter Frank Angell
629.	O's beat Oldham Athletic 5–3.
630.	Jimmy Bloomfield
631.	Two, against Mansfield Town and Sheffield United.
632.	Peter Charles Allen
633.	He is the O's all-time appearance record, League: 424(8) apps with 27 goals, FA Cup: 25 apps and 1 goal, League Cup: 24 apps with 1 goal and Anglo-Scottish Cup with 9 apps = 482 apps with 29 goals and unlikely to be broken.
634.	Tunji Babajide Banjo as a playing sub at Bolton Wanderers on 1 April.
635.	O's won 1–0 with a goal from Peter Kitchen.
636.	He scored a total of 29 goals, 21 in the League and 7 in the FA Cup and 1 in the League Cup.
637.	He is the last O's player to score 20 or more League goals in a season.
637A.	Glenn Victor Roeder for a reported £250,000.
638.	Full-back, Mark Stuart Smith
639.	Carlisle, on 4 April 1962.
640.	Bobby Fisher, Henry Hughton, John Chiedozie, Tunji Banjo and Kevin Godfrey, the latter as a sub who replace defender Mark Smith.
641.	Ralph Coates and Ian Richard Moores.
642.	He netted twice to secure an O's 2–0 win.
643.	John Peter Kane
643A.	Nigel Albert Meeking, he is semi-retired living on the Isle of Wight, the American player was Christopher James 'CJ' Carenza, today he works as a lawyer in St Louis, USA.
644.	O's won 2–0 with goals from Joe Mayo and John Chiedozie before 29,220 fans.
645.	O's lost 5–3 with goals from John Chiedozie (2) and Peter Kitchen.
646.	The sale of Peter Kitchen to fellow Second Division side Fulham for £150,000 plus a young Welshman.
647.	Mark Stuart Gray

648. No, he made just 1(1) League appearances, with 0 goals and was released in May 1981.

649. He trialled with Swansea City, played for Pembroke, went to Australia to play for Spearwood Dalmatinac FC, managed Pembroke, and was sales manager for Cardiff based Brains Brewery.

650. Alan Whittle, from the Perspolis club in Tehran, Iran.

651. 19,945, O's largest crowd of the season against Crystal Palace.

652. Tommy Taylor

653. Mervyn Richard Day for £100,000, at the time O's record transfer fee.

654. Assistant manager, Pater Frank Angell.

655. William John Jennings from West Ham United for £100,000 and John William Margerrison from Fulham for £65,000.

656. O's beat Fulham 1–0 with Ralph Coates scoring.

657. 5,090

658. Leslie Grade

659. Defender, Mark Penfold

660. Kevin Godfrey, on 29 December 1979 against Luton Town.

Answers to Chapter 12

661. Ralph Coates in a 1–0 win against Charlton Athletic on 12 January 1980.

662. Tommy Johnston's daughter Alison.

663. 3,779 against Swansea City on 30 April 1980, it ended 0–0.

664. Stanley Bowles from Nottingham Forest for £90,000.

665. 3–0, Billy Jennings, John Chiedozie and Ralph Coates.

666. None, they drew seven and lost three.

667. Four, Mervyn Day, Bobby Fisher, Tommy Taylor and Ralph Coates.

668. Her father Robin Jacques played for O's in the 1922–23 season, also being an RAF pilot he sadly died in an air crash in August 1923, aged 26, with his daughter Hattie just 18 months old.

669. Peter John Taylor for £150,000 from Tottenham Hotspur.

670. Queen's Park Rangers 4–0, with goals from John Chiedozie, Billy Jennings (2) and Peter Taylor.

671. 17th

672. John Chiedozie and Ian Moores with 9 goals each.

673. Olattunji Babajide Banjo and John Okechukwu Chiedozie against Tunisia in a World Cup qualifying game.

674. John Chiedozie for £600,000, paid by County in instalments.

675. He resigned after the transfer as he was against the deal.

676. Paul Went took over as caretaker manager.

677. Peter Taylor in a 2–1 win at Bradford City.

678. 11 games

679. 22 September 1991

680. He sacked manager Paul Went.

681. 21 days

682. As caretaker (League and League Cup): P6 W2 D2 L2 F6 A7. As full-time manager: P5 W0 D0 L5 F0 A10.

683. Joe Mayo to Cambridge United for £100,000.

684. Kenneth Knighton was appointed 13 October 1981.

685. Frank Albert Clark

686. On 7 November 1981, a 3–0 win over Sheffield Wednesday.

687. Stanley Bowles for a reported £80,000

688. 56 League and Cup appearances with 7 goals.

689. David Charles Giles, scored twice at Oldham Athletic in a 3–2 defeat while on loan from Swansea City.

690. Keith Morton Houchen for £25,000.

691. 5 May 1982, a 2–2 draw at Chelsea.

692. 6,009

693. Leicester City 3–0

694. Robert George Vincent

695. Bottom of Division Two with 39 points.

696. Ian Richard Moores with 9 League and Cup goals.

697. 12 January 1998

698. 2,090, versus Oldham Athletic on Saturday 15 May.

699.   William Robert Roffey
700.   18 goals
701.   John East Hawley from Arsenal and Trevor Carl Lee from Gillingham.
702.   O's lost 1–5 on 23 October 1982.
703.   Michael Peter Kitchen to secure victory in a 2–1 win over Preston North End on 17 December 1982.
704.   Mark Christopher Blackhall in the 5–2 defeat at Brentford.
705.   James Anthony Mankelow
706.   Walthamstow Avenue
707.   David James Price
708.   O's won 4–1 with goals from Houchen, Kitchen, Godfrey and Roffey before 4,468 fans.
709.   Reading, who ended on 53 points, one fewer than O's.
710.   Mervyn Day to Leeds United.
711.   197 League and Cup games between July 1979 and May 1983.
712.   He was a co-commentator on ESPN's coverage of Bundesliga games, having left his job as chief scout for Leeds United the previous month.
713.   Richard Martin Key from Cambridge United.
714.   No, Raymond King played against Northampton Town on 2 November 1946, but broke his wrist; he later made a name for himself with Port Vale.
715.   Frank Albert Clark
716.   Kevin Peter Hales joined from Chelsea.
717.   353(16) League and Cup appearances with 26 goals.
718.   It was centre-half Tommy Cunningham who scored a hat-trick.
719.   Peter Kitchen netted four goals in a 5–3 win over Millwall.
720.   Michael Leonard Mancini, brother of Terry.
721.   Peter Kitchen with 13 League and Cup goals.
722.   Patrick Corbett and Kevin Hales with 43 appearances each.
723.   Avalon
724.   O's lost 4–5
725.   Ian Martin Juryeff

726. Kevin Godfrey, in a 4–3 win against Bolton Wanderers.

727. O's drew 0–0 and were relegated instead of Swansea City.

728. Never before, the 1985–86 season would be the first time.

729. 2,640

730. Peter Charles Wells

731. Millwall

732. Paul Shinners from Gillingham

733. Richard Raymond Cadette

734. Netted 4 goals against O's in their 5–1 home win in August 1985.

735. 1,443

736. Stephen Charles Castle bagged all four goals in O's 4–1 win at Rochdale on 5 May 1986.

737. In fifth position on 72 points.

738. That they were close to going into liquidation.

739. Life-long O's fan Anthony Wood, a 59-year-old coffee merchant and Honorary Consul for the UK Government in Rwanda bought 76 per cent interest in the club from the Ovenden family.

739A. Former chairman, Brian Winston.

740. Terence Howard from Chelsea.

741. Alan Comfort with 11 League goals.

742. Burnley beat O's 2–1, a match covered live on the BBC World Service radio.

743. They changed their name from Orient back to Leyton Orient.

744. Their 1,000th Football League victory when they defeated Newport County 4–1.

745. 8–0

746. Smalley, Shinners, Hales (pen), Hales, Dickinson, Comfort, Comfort and Shinners.

747. Ian Martin Juryeff

748. O's lost 0–2

749. The attendance of 7,738, was O's highest home attendance of the season.

750. Michael David Marks

751. Brian Eastick

751A.   Head coach of the England Under-20s side.
752.   Alan Edward Hull
753.   Kevin Joseph Campbell
754.   Mark David Cooper
755.   O's finished in sixth spot and so reached the Play-offs for the first time.
756.   Scarborough, 2–1 on aggregate.
757.   Mark Cooper scored twice.
758.   Daniel Stephen Carter
759.   Drew 0–0
760.   Lee Derek Harvey and Mark Cooper.
761.   Jon Bowden
762.   Paul Terence Ward
763.   Alan Hull
763A.   Alan Comfort

Answers to Chapter 13

764.   After five straight wins at home, O's lost 0–1 to Bolton Wanderers on 20 October 1990.
765.   Christopher Gerald Bart-Williams in a 4–0 win over Tranmere Rovers.
766.   16 years and 232 days
767.   Paul Mark Cobb
768.   In June 2012 he was an Asbestos Surveyor, he checks in households and commercial properties for any of the banned material.
769.   Gregory John Berry scored a hat-trick against Bury.
770.   Ricky Junior Otto, as a playing substitute on 11 May 1991.
771.   Terence Howard, with 57 League and Cup games.
772.   Peter Eustace
773.   Kevin Nugent 4 and Andrew Sayer 3.
774.   2 points
775.   Chris Bart-Williams for £350,000.
776.   Goalkeeper, Christopher Robert Turner.
777.   Brentford

778.   O's won 4–2

779.   A major brawl involving 16 players occurred and Kenneth Achampong was 'unluckily' sent off.

780.   David Roland Elleray

781.   Stephen Patrick Okai

782.   4,460

782A.   David Edward Samuel Kitchen (always known as Sam)

783.   They rose from fifth position to top spot of Division Two.

784.   1,806

785.   Three, Terry Howard, Robert Taylor and Ricky Otto.

786.   Robert Taylor with 18 goals.

787.   Seventh position on 72 points.

788.   Bernie Dixon, the youth manager and club scout.

789.   Ricky Otto was sold to Southend United.

790.   Manager Peter Eustace was sacked.

791.   Assistant manager Chris Turner and youth team manager John Sitton took over.

792.   Joint caretaker managers

793.   Once, a 2–1 home win against Swansea City, this from five games.

794.   Colin West with 14 League goals from 42(1) appearances.

795.   They beat the eventual champions Birmingham City 2–1.

796.   Just five more games against, Bournemouth, Chester City, Cardiff City, Peterborough United, and Shrewsbury Town.

797.   They could not loan or buy any players due to a League embargo, this because of a financial crisis at the club and players wages could not be paid.

798.   Chairman and owner Tony Wood's coffee business in Rwanda had collapsed due to the civil unrest in that country.

799.   Firstly, the Professional Footballers' Association, and then Philip Wallace a local businessman, who took over the running of the club for two months in order to look at the O's books.

800.   O's owed £500,000, and were losing £10,000 per week.

801.   He said that the club's financial situation was far too severe for him to take over, and so he pulled out of a deal with Wood.

801A.   Stevenage
802.   Barry Hearn
803.   £5, plus paying off all the debts.
804.   Orient: Club for a Fiver
805.   Ms Jo Treharne, she started in August 1994 and finished it a year later. A graduate in Media Studies. She recently spoke to me from home in Kent.

'I chose Orient because it was the closest club to my house at the time. I thought Tony Wood was a lovely man, a very caring person, warm and witty. He made me feel very welcome and had no ego. He had a great affection and passion for the club. He was very worried at the time at the civil war in Rwanda and on the human and economic cost to the people, more than the economic loss to himself, which was huge. There were many incidents which I was asked to leave out but the stuff I did catch for the film were definitely not staged for the camera, they were immediate and real and yes I was there when Terry Howard got sacked. On reflection, I wish I had never made the film at all. Today, I'm married to DP member in Canterbury, Kent, Alex Perkins, and work as Communications Manager for the NHS Eastern and Coastal in Kent, I'm also raising my kids and just being plain boring at over 40.'

806.   Mark Warren, who netted a hat-trick
807.   They sacked long-serving defender Terence Howard
808.   401(6) League and Cup games with 36 goals
809.   Signed by Wycombe Wanderers manager Martin O'Neill.
810.   He sacked both Sitton and Turner.
811.   P48 W7 D9 L32 F33 A79 Pts 30
812.   First-team player, Glenn Cockerill and youth team manager Thomas Loizou.
813.   One, a 1–0 defeat at Bristol Rovers on 22 April 1995.
814.   Patrick George Holland
815.   None, in fact they gained only two draws with 21 defeats.

816. 26 points
817. Nyree Anthony Okpara Kelly, his fee was £30,000.
818. Russell Kelly, who joined from Chelsea on non-contract terms in March 1996.
819. Mark Leon Watson, scored at Plymouth Argyle but then returned back to West Ham United.
820. 42 League games
821. Alexander Inglethorpe
822. None, they drew 7 and lost 15 games.
823. Roger Edmund Stanislaus
824. On 1 February 1996, he was given a 12 month ban and he was fired by O's.
825. He had an unsuccessful trial with Peterborough United and then became a counsellor to the homeless and hopeless in Hammersmith, London.
826. 2,121, the lowest attendance at Brisbane Road for nine years.
827. Nigerian born Samuel Tayo Ayorinde.
828. Sturm Graz of Austria.
829. O's beat the Wales first team by 2–1.
830. Three trialists were involved, Aidey Boothroyd passed to Gregory Tello, he crossed the ball, and it fell to Peter Garland to scramble the ball home.
831. £26,000
832. A profit of £11,638 was made.
833. Alvin Edward Martin and Alan Jesse Sealey.
834. Martin was 36 and Sealey 38.
835. Alan William Sealey, they were cousins.
836. Alan died aged 53 in 1996 and Les died aged 43 in 2001.
837. Martin Ling
838. Steven Alexander Riches
839. They went six hours without scoring a goal.
840. He sacked manager Pat Holland.
841. P63 W16 D16 L31 F54 A78 Pts64
842. Thomas Edward Cunningham, P2 W1 D0 L1 F1 A1 Pts3
843. Carl Brian Griffiths, on loan from Peterborough United.

844.   Thomas Frederick Taylor

845.   Paul Peterson Clark

846.   Andrew Buonocore, known to one-and-all as Buono who later became the tannoy announcer/DJ.

847.   Scott McGleish

848.   Les Sealey

849.   He became the oldest player to play for O's in the League, aged 47 years and 72 days in the 3–0 victory over Cardiff City on 30 November 1996.

850.   He became the first English player to achieve the feat of making 1,000 career League appearances.

851.   1,005 League games

852.   333 clean sheets

853.   Bjørn Olav Heidenstrøm

854.   Raymond Colin Wilkins

855.   A pitch invasion when three O's players were attacked by Brighton hooligans.

856.   Paul Anthony Atkin on loan from York City, Christopher Bryan Timons (non-contract), David Ellison Morrison, a £20,000 signing from Peterborough United and Leopold Fortune-West on loan from Gillingham.

857.   40 players

858.   Stephen Brian Hodge

859.   Craig Thomas Richardson

860.   Michael John Williams

861.   Five times

862.   Mark Nicholas Cooper

863.   Goalkeeper, Luke Dennis Spencer Weaver

864.   He broke his jaw and during a two-year stay in the North-East he never once played for their first team.

865.   Darren Edward Pitcher

866.   Darren John Purse and the amount was £120,000.

867.   Carl Griffiths with 21 League and Cup goals.

868.   Secretary David Burton failed to inform manager Taylor that three players, Mark Warren, Simon Clark and Stuart Hicks all should have been suspended for the visit to Exeter City

on 31 January 1998, Clark scored one of the goals and Exeter City complained to the FA.

869. He resigned

870. Loyal club servant, Frank Woolf.

871. Patrick Kwame Ampadu

872. Wim Walschaerts

873. The Scotsman on loan from Dundee was Stephen McCormick and the American was David Eugene Junior McDougald.

874. Amara Sylla Simba

875. Steven Watts

876. O's reached the promotion Play-offs.

877. Rotherham United

878. Scott Barrett

879. Dean Smith, Martin Ling, Dave Morrison and Matthew Lockwood.

880. Alejandro Calvo-Garcia

881. 36,985

882. No, they played two League games back in November and December 1930.

883. Iyseden Christie, Alfreton Town

884. £40,000

885. Joshua Davie Low

885A. Bath City

886. Andrew David Douglas Harris

887. A sports teacher at the Kingston Maurward College in Dorset and coach at Dorchester Town FC.

888. Gavin Victor Holligan and Daniel Hockton.

889. Ahmet Brkovic

890. He met a girl from Romford while she was on holiday in that country, they fell in love and got married and moved to Essex.

891. David McGhee, his nickname was 'Mad Dog'.

892. Carl Griffiths was signed from Port Vale for £80,000.

893. 5–1 at Chester City on 28 December 1999.

894. Carl Griffiths, including two penalties.

895. Four victories

Answers to Chapter 14

896.   Steve Watts on 37 minutes in a 3–1 win at Exeter City on 8 January 2000. The other scorers were Dean Smith (55 mins) and Iyseden Christie (90 mins).

897.   Jabo Oshevire Ibehre, Jade 'Jay' Alan Murray, Ronald Donald Gould, Aaron McLean and David Parsons.

898.   Aaron McLean with Hull City, he joined them from Peterborough United for over £1 million in January 2011.

899.   In 2006 he was jailed for seven years for raping a woman at her home while working as a postman. He was released under license in 2009, but in February 2010 he was arrested for assaulting a woman in a Holloway pub and later sentenced to two years to run concurrently with the remainder of his seven year jail term.

900.   Richard Garcia

901.   He snapped his cruciate knee ligaments.

902.   Jabo Ibehre

903.   Hull's John Eyre

904.   O's won 2–1 with goals from Steve Watts header and a cracking shot from Matthew Lockwood.

905.   The Millennium Stadium, Cardiff on 26 May 2001.

906.   Christopher Douglas Tate

907.   4–2

908.   12 players, Harris (South Africa), Walchaerts (Belgium), Brkovic (Croatia), Garcia (Australia), McElholm (Northern Ireland), Cadiou (France), Opara (Nigeria), Mansley (Australia), Pinamonte (Italy), Vasseur (France), Opinel (France) and Forge (France).

909.   Stephen Castle

910.   Stéphane Leoni

911.   Matthew Lockwood, having missed a penalty, he scored from the rebound.

912.   The Referee ordered the spot-kick to be retaken. This one was also missed but this time by Jeffrey Simon Minton.

913.   Paul Brush

914.   Jeff Minton

915. They lost them all, at Bristol Rovers 5–3, at Hartlepool United 3–1, at Carlisle United 6–1, home to Cheltenham Town 0–2 and at Lincoln City 2–0.

916. In a disappointing 18th position.

917. Gary Fletcher

918. He married Viv Taylor and to show his love for her changed his name to Gary Taylor-Fletcher.

919. Lee Anthony Thorpe and Jamal Julian Campbell-Ryce.

920. Ezomo 'Izzy' Iriekpen

921. Gary George Alexander

922. He netted a hat-trick on 5 April to secure a vital 3–2 win over Boston United.

923. Gregory James Heald and Michael Thomas Turner.

924. Ciaran Toner, 4 June 2003 against Italy and 11 June against Spain.

925. O's had two players sent off, Gary Alexander and Matthew Lockwood.

926. Chairman Hearn fired Paul Brush on Saturday 27 September 2003.

927. His assistant Martin Ling took over.

928. He sent a message of best wishes to Ling.

929. O's won 1–0 at Carlisle United on 30 September 2003.

930. Two own-goals from Drewe Broughton and Testaye Bramble.

931. Gary Alexander

932. They went top of the table, the first time since 17 October 1992.

933. Lee Anthony James Steele

934. He went to the top of the League Two goalscoring charts with 11 goals, one more than Junior Agogo of Bristol Rovers, the first O's player to achieve this feat since Peter Kitchen back in the 1977–78 season.

935. Scott Peter Fitzgerald, on month's loan from Watford, he was sent off on 75 minutes and did not wear an O's first-team shirt again.

936. Scott Edward Wallis

937.   Lee Steele for his 17 League and Cup goals.
938.   Andrew Scott
939.   It was their 90th
940.   Craig Easton
941.   Joseph Richard Keith
942.   He picked up a weak back pass, rounded goalkeeper Alan Fettis and stopped on the goalline having his picture taken with the O's mascot Theo the Wyvern and only then back-heeling the ball into the empty net for the winner.
943.   Manager of the Month after his team were unbeaten.
944.   In third spot behind leaders Wycombe Wanderers and second placed Grimsby Town.
945.   Paul Connor and Adam John Tann.
946.   Lowly Rushden & Diamonds beat O's 1–0 on 18 March.
947.   With three minutes into stoppage time Northampton gained a corner, David Hunt sent over the ball and there was Ryan Gilligan to stab the ball home for a 1–1 draw. At Oxford in the final seconds the ball found its way to Gary Alexander on the left wing, he passed the ball into the penalty area for an unmarked Lee Steele to slide the ball past Billy Turley to secure a 3–2 win and automatic promotion.
948.   Away victory number 363.
949.   Russell Slade
950.   Glyn Garner when he came on at 46 minutes to replace Jason Brown against Trinidad & Tobago.
951.   Gabriel Abdala Zakuani for £1 million, rising by a further £500,000, dependent on appearances.
952.   None
953.   David William Partridge
954.   No, he was on loan from Dundee in January 2002 and got himself sent off against Swansea City the following month.
955.   Lee Steele scored on 45 minutes against Millwall on 8 August 2006.
956.   Gary Taylor-Fletcher
957.   Adam John Tann
958.   Bottom with 15 points.

959.   They won 3–1.

960.   Luke Gutteridge, Adam Chambers and Wayne Corden.

961.   Simon

962.   Lee Steele joined Chester City, Joe Keith moved to Brentford, Paul Connor went to Cheltenham Town and Daryl McMahon joined Stevenage Borough.

963.   Paul Connor for £20,000.

964.   £25,000

965.   Philip Patrick Stephen Mulrayne

966.   Training to become a catholic priest.

967.   He netted a hat-trick in O's remarkable 5–2 victory.

968.   Gary Alexander for O's on 5 minutes and an own-goal for the Lions on 66 minutes.

969.   Gary Alexander (62 mins) and Adam Tann (65 mins).

970.   Donovan Ricketts, O's tried to sign him in March 2002, but he was denied a work permit.

971.   Tom Kemp, Jack Page and Solomon Joel Anthony Shields.

972.   Two, Solomon Shields replaced Aiden Palmer at half-time, he got injured on 72 minutes and was replaced by Jack Page.

973.   Matthew Dominic Lockwood

974.   FL: 327(9) apps, 51 goals (incl Play-offs), FA Cup: 25 apps, 2 goals, League Cup: 15 apps 2 goals, Other Cups: 9 apps 2 goals

Lockwood holds two O's records, one the record for the most converted penalties by an O's player, with 32, nine more than Ken Facey. And secondly the most goals scored by a defender of 57 League and Cup goals, Dean Smith being in second place with 37 League and Cup goals.

975.   Tamika Paul Makandawire, J.J. Melligan, Paul Laurence Terry and Stuart James Nelson.

976.   John Joseph

977.   A free transfer

978.   Sean Thornton, with a spectacular 30 yard free-kick on 38 minutes.

979.   It was O's 5,000th Football League goal.

980.   Andrew Barcham against Luton Town.

981.   Loick Pires, on 19 April against Doncaster Rovers.

982.   Six, Boyd 5 and Wayne William Gray 1.

983.   Boyd with 17 goals, 14 League, 2 FA Cup and 1 League Cup.

984.   Adam Craig Chambers with 45 League appearances 5(1) Cup appearances = 50(1) appearances.

985.   Efe Echanomi

986.   Grimsby Town

987.   Daniel Patrick Granville, Ryan Robert Jarvis, Andrew Robert Cave-Brown and James Lewis Jones.

988.   Simon Jonathan Dawkins Jnr

989.   J.J. Melligan

990.   Jack Charles Jeffery, he replaced Melligan on 24 minutes.

991.   None, he picked up an injury in that match and returned to Upton Park.

991A.   Thomas Bourhill Johnston, they named their South Stand, The Tommy Johnston Stand.

992.   Dean Lance Morgan

993.   Manager Martin Ling and his assistant Dean Smith were both fired on 18 January 2009.

994.   Kevin Nugent as caretaker manager for the next three League games.

995.   Terry Byrne

996.   No

997.   Milton Keynes Dons, with a 2–1 win at the Stadium MK.

998.   Samuel Parkin, he made 12(1) League appearances without scoring.

999.   David Geraint Williams

1,000. He won seven of the first 10 League games in charge.

1,001. Serbia and Slovakia

1,002. He became O's 1,000th player to appear in League, FA Cup and League Cup appearances over 104 years after first entering the FA Cup in 1904 and the Football League in 1905.

1,003. Twenty-three passes were made and the ball was touched by every O's player before McGleish scored from inside the six-yard box. The move spanned one minute and 17 seconds.

1,004.   Simon Church

1,005.   The goal was originally awarded to Sean Thornton, but his free-kick took a slight deflection off Church, and so, it was awarded to Church by the Dubious Goals Panel, sorry Sean?

1,006.   Jason William Robert Crowe

1,007.   Jason Demetriou made 42(1)=43 League appearances, Purches made 42 appearances.

1,008.   Adam Boyd with 12 League and Cup goals.

1,009.   In 14th position

1,010.   9,271

1,011.   Adrian Marion Pâtulea, he was born in Tárgoviste, Romania.

1,012.   Andros Darryl Townsend

1,013.   On 42 minutes he picked up the ball on the left side from inside his own half, he ran 70 yards beating three defenders and went on to score a wonderful solo goal.

1,014.   Goalie James Lewis Jones received a head injury and after more than four minutes of treatment left the field to be replaced by Glenn James Morris.

1,015.   Matthew Anthony Briggs from Fulham and Nicholas William Adams from Leicester City.

1,016.   Briggs made one start and Adams six starts.

1,016A. Crawley Town

1,017.   Jonathan Kahne Téhoué

1,018.   J.J. Melligan

1,019.   Tamika Mkandawire

1,020.   Eric Joseph Lichaj from Aston Villa and John William Spicer from Doncaster Rovers.

1,021.   Poland, both his parents were born in the southern Polish town of Nowy Targ.

1,022.   Manager Geraint Williams was fired.

1,023.   Kevin Nugent

1,024.   Russell Slade

1,025.   He was given a contract until the end of the season with a mandate to save O's from relegation.

1,026.   O's avoided relegation by one point finishing in 17th position, very well done Russ.

1,027.   Midland Football Alliance side Armitage 90 FC.

1,028.   League One Manager of the Year with Yeovil Town.

1,029.   Scott McGleish with 12 League goals.

1,030.   On 14 May 2010 he signed a two-year contract.

1,031.   George Edwards Porter

1,032.   St Mary's Hospital, Sidcup, Kent (not London as stated in a number of profiles).

1,033.   Jason Demetriou joined Cyprus club AEK Larnaca.

1,034.   Alexander David Revell

1,034A. Robert 'Bobby' Moss

1,035.   Liddle was born in Hounslow, Middlesex and he played one League game two days after he was signed, a 2–1 defeat at Yeovil Town, he picked up a late injury in the match and returned to Sunderland.

1,036.   Paul-Jose Ebunge Mpoku

1,037.   Belgium

1,038.   Andrew James Ker Frampton

1,039.   James Luke Newton Walker

1,040.   Benjamin Francis Chorley

1,041.   Andrew John Whing

1,042.   Jason Roy Brown came on loan from Blackburn Rovers.

1,043.   George Henry Poulton died on 3 December, aged 80 and Harold Edward Pole died on 16 October aged 88.

1,044.   Thomas James Carroll and Harry Edward Kane.

1,045.   4–0 against Sheffield Wednesday

1,045A. Adrian Marian Patulea

1,046.   O's former vice-chairman Nicholas Levene, who has admitted to fraud totaling £32 million, his case is due to be heard in late October 2012.

1,047.   Adam Nicholas Barrett

1,048.   Gabby Zakuani

1,049.   Steve Zakuani, who is now playing in America.

1,050.   Seventh

1,051.   No, seventh was their highest position.

1,052. Dean Cox with 53 League and Cup appearances.

1,053. Scott McGleish with 17 League and Cup goals.

1,054. Dean Cox, with 19 assists in the League and three in Cup competition.

1,055. Stephen Dawson

1,056. Moses Adeshina Odubajo

1,057. Championship side Barnsley

1,058. Ryan Jarvis, Scott McGleish, Aaron Brown, Harry Beautyman, Jason Crowe and Joshua Millwood.

1,059. Josh Millwood

1,060. Leon McSweeney

1,061. A two metre high solid granite memorial dedicated to the service of players and supporters of Clapton Orient FC who fell during World War One.

1,062. Millwall's Marc James Peter Laird on a two-year contract.

1,063. Disastrously, they went 10 League games without a win.

1,064. 33-year-old Kevin Anthony Lisbie

1,065. 1 October 2012, 2–1 against Preston North End.

1,066. They were unbeaten during five League games.

1,067. Six minutes into stoppage time, on 90+6 minutes.

1,068. David Mooney scored twice, the second from the penalty spot.

1,069. Elliott Junior Omozusi. He was sentenced to 30 months in prison after being found guilty of intimidating a witness who helped convict members of the London Fields Boys Gang, that he was a member of. The gang had murdered schoolgirl Agnes Sina-Inakoju in Hoxton, London.

1,070. Charles John Daniels

1,071. Around £200,000

1,072. Manager Russell Slade signed a new two and half year contract on 29 November and the following day Kevin Lisbie signed a new contract until 30 May 2013.

1,073. Kevin Lisbie on 65 and 87 minutes.

1,074. Matthew John Spring

1,075. Stevenage

1,076. Dean Leacock, Syam Habib Ben Youseff and Solomon Oldiran Taiwo.

1,077. Ryan Anthony Dickson

1,078. Defender, Scott Cuthbert, and he kept a clean-sheet.

1,079. Glenn Cockerill

1,080. Two yellow cards on 84 and 85 minutes, he was then sent off.

1,081. They lost five games.

1,082. Alan Judge

1,083. Calvin Hyden Andrew

1,084. He made 2(8) League appearances, without finding the net.

1,085. One shot

1,086. Jamal Julian Campbell-Ryce from Bristol City and Adam Michael Reed from Sunderland.

1,087. Jamie Peter Smith

1,088. One, he came on as sub in the 3–0 defeat at Exeter City to replace David Mooney at 85 minutes on 9 April 2012 and played a total of 8 minutes and 49 seconds.

1,089. Moses Odubajo

1,090. Afolabi Obafemi and Billy Jay Lobjoit.

1,091. Doncaster Rovers

1,092. Six, Benjamin Robert Alnwick (on loan from Tottenham Hotspur), Lee Butcher, David Robert Edmund Button (on loan from Tottenham Hotspur), Jamie Jones, Paul Stephen Rachubka (on loan from Leeds United) and Marek Stech (on loan from West Ham United).

1,093. Thomas Lovelock, he joined Sutton United.

1,094. Scott Cuthbert

1,095. Matthew Spring with 45 League and Cup appearances. Wycombe Wanderers.

1,096. Kevin Lisbie with 12 League goals.

1,097. 26-year-old Gary Dean Sawyer, a defender who had turned down a new deal with Bristol Rovers.

1,098. Enfield, north London, his family moved to Bideford in Devon at a young age.

1,099. No, Lee Thomas Sawyer, the former Chelsea player was on trial with O's on 14 December 2012, playing for O's reserves in the 1–1 draw against Wycombe Wanderers.

1,100.   Midfielder Anthony James Griffith, he was their player of the year in 2010.

1,101.   Montserrat, he played two matches against Belize in the 2014 World Cup qualifying matches to be held in Brazil, losing 8–3 on aggregate.

1,102.   Sixty-five-year-old Graham Stanley Ballard.

1,103.   Kevin Levi Austin

1,103A.   The O's Supporters Club chairman is David Dodd and his deputy is Stephen Jenkins.

1,103B.   Denis Rofe

1,103C.   Julian Lloyd Webber

Answers to Chapter 15

1,104.   The Middlesex Senior Cup

1,105.   Crouch End Vampires 3–1

1,106.   The West Ham Charity Cup, defeating Clapton FC 1–0 at their Spotted Dog Ground and beating Ealing 1–0 to win the Middlesex County Charity Cup.

1,107.   1871

1,108.   Enfield at home on 17 September 1904.

1,109.   O's won 4–1, the first FA Cup goal was scored by Jack William Reynolds.

1,110.   Home to Leytonstone by 1–1, O's won the away replay 5–2.

1,111.   Hitchin Town by 2–1

1,112.   Barking 3–1, Leyton 3–1 and Clapton 2–0.

1,113.   Chesterfield Town

1,114.   O's lost 3–0, during the tie the referee had to stop play a number of times due to the players fighting on the pitch.

1,115.   The FA ordered that ties had to be played on the same day as League games and that the first team must play in the FA Cup and a reserve side in the League.

1,116.   O's first team beat Custom House 3–0 in the FA Cup and the reserve lost in the League 3–0 at West Brom.

1,117.   O's won 5–2, they were a school side located in Leyton and the team comprised of old boys of the Newport Secondary

School who were known as 'The News'. They were winners of the Leyton League in 1899.

1,118.   Stockport born William Edley

1,119.   Harold Halse

1,120.   Left-back, Thomas Worley Stewart

1,121.   The 4th Battalion King's Royal Rifles who were based in Essex.

1,122.   The London Challenge Cup

1,123.   Millwall, 3–0

1,124.   Fog had descended around Millfields Road and visibility was down to zero. The referee abandoned the match after 55 minutes, with the Gunners leading 1–0.

1,125.   O's forward Ron Goffin.

1,126.   Woolwich Arsenal by 2–1

1,127.   The match was re-run at the local Clapton Bioscope where thousands went to watch.

1,128.   6–0

1,129.   This was O's heaviest ever defeat since joining the League in 1905, a total of 305 League and FA Cup games.

1,130.   Edwin 'Ted' Davis

1,131.   O's forward Willie Jonas bundled goalie Joseph Orme and the ball into the net and started to celebrate a goal, but Orme got up and punched the O's player who retaliated by kicking Orme, a number of players starting fighting and many of O's 5,000 away contingent attacked the Millwall fans with police on horseback called in to separate the fighting fans with many arrests made. In the end both the players were sent off, the goal was disallowed and the referee blew his whistle to end the rough affair.

1,132.   The attendance of 36,800 was a then ground record.

1,133.   O's lost in the second replay 2–1, the game being played at White Hart Lane before over 12,000 fans.

1,134.   Owen Williams

1,135.   O's beat high-flying Newcastle United 2–0 before 31,420 fans, the goals were scored by John McDonald Galbraith and Donald James Cock.

1,136.   O's lost 1–6 at home to Manchester City.

1,137. On an icy pitch O's drew 0–0 before a Villa Park crowd of 53,086, being the highest attendance ever to watch an O's game up to that point.

1,138. O's lost 0–8 at Millfields Road, still O's heaviest ever defeat.

1,139. It took three games, O's winning 4–1 in a second replay at Highbury.

1,140. O's lost 4–1 before a 48,141 St James' Park crowd.

1,141. In preventing a certain goal he crashed against an upright and broke his collarbone.

1,142. Clifford Harold Blackwell, he is famous for holding an umbrella and wearing a raincoat during a thunderstorm while Aberdeen were thrashing Peterhead by 13 goals.

1,143. Southern Section Cup (North and South)

1,144. Norwich City away on Thursday 8 February, O's lost 3–0.

1,145. James Bow, a 25-year-old Scotsman.

1,146. O's beat Charlton Athletic 3–0 with goals from Harold Taylor and Thomas Curtis Foster with two goals.

1,147. The 18,658 crowd was a record for the Lea Bridge Road ground.

1,148. O's won 2–0 at Southend United before a crowd of 2,068 with two goals from reserve winger Frederick William Fisher.

1,149. They asked QPR if they could play their reserve goalie at the time, John Gilfillan; a quick phone call to the FA and permission was granted, O's lost 2–0.

1,150. York City, O's drew 2–2 before 7,713 fans.

1,151. O's won the first leg at home 2–1 but lost away in the second-leg 2–0, and so surprisingly went out 3–2 on aggregate.

1,152. Les Gore and Henry Harold Parr with a penalty.

1,153. The Essex Professional Cup

1,154. Clacton Town

1,155. George Adams 2, Edward John Connolly 2, James Smith 2 and John George Dryden 1.

1,156. Gorleston

1,157. Dennis Frank Pacey

1,158. Welshman, William Derek Rees
1,159. Everton, after a 0–0 at Brisbane Road, O's went to Goodison Park and won 3–1 before 39,750 fans.
1,160. Thomas Harris and two goals from Dennis Pacey.
1,161. O's won 1–0 with Harris on the score sheet again.
1,162. 49,500
1,163. O's borrowed Arsenal's red with white sleeved shirts.
1,164. Arsenal, O's lost 0–3 before an all-ticket 30,000 home sell-out.
1,165. O's beat Fulham 2–1, David Ivor Davies scored, he made just five senior appearances in his O's career and this was his only goal.
1,166. £819.00
1,167. Albert Leake with a mishit shot.
1,168. Raymond King
1,169. An own-goal from Owen Fitz.
1,170. Lovells Athletic
1,171. Ronald Ernest Heckman
1,172. The Southern Floodlight Challenge Cup
1,173. John Hartburn
1,174. Brian Webb, he left O's in December 1958 to join Ramsgate.
1,175. O's lost 4–1 with Jimmy Andrews scoring.
1,176. Joseph Cini, he did not like the cold weather so returned home after a couple of months. In later years he went on to win 18 caps for Malta and scored two goals. He also played in the English League for Queen's Park Rangers having been signed by Alec Stock in 1959.
1,177. Edward Lewis
1,178. Tommy Johnston
1,179. Terry McDonald, Tommy Johnston and Phil White.
1,180. Malcolm Musgrove with two, Phil Woosnam one and an own-goal from Ken Facey.
1,181. Ken Facey with seven appearances, followed by Bishop and Groombridge on five each.
1,182. Eddy Brown and Tommy Johnston scored two goals each.
1,183. O's drew 2–2 at Chester.
1,184. Ronald Edmund Foster

1,185. Terence James McDonald
1,186. 6–2 with goals from Joe Elwood 2, Eddie Lewis 2 'pens',
        Tommy Johnston and Terry McDonald.
1,187. O's won 1–0 with a cracking shot from Derek William
        Gibbs.
1,188. Wednesday's big centre-forward Keith Ellis barged Frank
        George, who was holding the ball, into the net for their
        second goal, which the referee awarded.
1,189. 5–1
1,190. Burnley
1,191. 9–2
1,192. Malcolm Graham 3, George Edward Waites 3, David
        Dunmore 2 and Norman Deeley 1.
1,193. Roger Wedge
1,194. Bury
1,195. Between the end of December 1962 and February 1963 all
        sport being halted due to a big freeze.
1,196. Leicester City by 1–0
1,197. Malcolm Musgrove for his two goals.
1,198. Norman Victor Deeley on 90 seconds.
1,199. 5ft 5in
1,200. Peter Brabrook
1,201. It was a ground breaking attendance for Brisbane Road of
        34,345 with record receipts of £6,128.
1,202. O's lost 3–0 before 35,383 fans.
1,203. 1–1 before 7,420 fans.
1,204. Owen Simpson floated over a cross which home goalie
        Norman Oakes fumbled into his net, the goal was awarded
        to Simpson.
1,205. Victor Lewis Halom
1,206. Terence John 'Henry' Mancini and Vic Halom.
1,207. Roy Massey
1,208. Edwin Werge, sadly he died on 2 May 2007, aged 71.
1,209. Four goals.
1,210. Fulham, 1–0, before 12,901 Brisbane Road fans.
1,211. O's won at Sunderland 3–0 with goals from Barrie Edward

Fairbrother, John Barry Dyson and Mark Lazarus.

1,212. Three times, the first game in Nottingham ended 1–1, the replay at Brisbane Road on 25 January was abandoned at half-time due to a waterlogged pitch and, on 1 February Forest won 1–0.

1,213. The three Cup ties were watched by a total of 62,079 fans.

1,214. O's won at Filbert Street 2–0 with goals from Ian Bowyer and Peter Allen before 31,402 fans.

1,215. Barrie Fairbrother

1,216. O's hit the woodwork three times in the game.

1,217. Leonard Anthony Tompkins with a headed goal.

1,218. Gordon George Riddick with two goals.

1,219. Robert Leonard Arber

1,220. Due to a National electricians strike, which brought the country to a standstill, the first tie on 27 January, which ended 0–0, was played on a Sunday at Pompey and attracted 32,838 fans, including over 30 coach loads of O's fans. The replay was played on Tuesday afternoon on 29 January and ended 1–1.

1,221. O's lost 2–0, a game played at Crystal Palace's Selhurst Park.

1,222. The Texaco Cup

1,223. At West Ham United, O's lost 1–0 before 16,338 fans.

1,224. Laurence Paul Cunningham

1,225. Barrie Fairbrother, in a 2–1 defeat at Southampton.

1,226. The Anglo-Scottish Cup

1,227. Fulham 2–1 and Chelsea 2–1.

1,228. Derek James Possee

1,229. Phil Hoadley

1,230. Derek Possee and Laurie Cunningham.

1,231. Aberdeen

1,232. 15 October 1976, O's won at Aberdeen 1–0 with Derek Clarke scoring, in the second leg O's also won 1–0 through a Gerry Queen goal.

1,233. Partick Thistle

1,234. In the first leg O's won away with a goal from Laurie

Cunningham, in the second leg O's won 3–2 with goals from Alan Whittle and Gerry Queen 2 (1 pen).

1,235. Stratford born youth goalie John Holmes.

1,235A. Nottingham Forest

1,236. Derek Possee with a header.

1,237. Frank Clark

1,238. The floodlights failed.

1,239. 4–0

1,240. Millwall won 3–0

1,241. Barrie Fairbrother

1,242. Peter Allen

1,243. O's won 3–0 at White Hart Lane. Alan Whittle scored two, one an excellent overhead kick, and Bill Roffey.

1,244. John Smeulders

1,245. O's went to Norwich City and won a replay 1–0 through a Peter Kitchen goal, he also scored in the first game.

1,246. Blackburn Rovers 3–1, with goals from Kitchen 2, Joe Mayo 1.

1,247. John 'Stonewall' Jackson

1,248. William Roffey scored an own-goal for Chelsea.

1,249. Peter Kitchen

1,250. Arsenal

1,251. O's lost 3–0, 49,698 fans and the gate receipts were £147,225.

1,252. Goalkeeper, Ray Goddard

1,253. O's beat Bristol City before 1,999 fans with a goal from John Okechukwu Chiedozie.

1,254. Billy Jennings

1,255. Ray Bruce

1,256. Joe Mayo

1,257. Sean Rafter

1,258. The Football League Groups Cup.

1,259. O's beat Southend United 2–0 on 15 August 1981 before 1,806 fans, goals William John Jennings and John Chiedozie.

1,260. Pat Rice, an own-goal.

1,261. Once only against Southend, they drew two and lost three.

1,262. Associate Members' Cup

1,263. Just one
1,264. At Brentford, O's lost 3–2 with two goals from Peter Kitchen.
1,265. Patrick George Holland
1,266. Newport County, the Welsh side won 4–2 in a penalty shoot-out before 1,272 Brisbane Road fans.
1,267. Barry Silkman and Neil Banfield.
1,268. Dean Greygoose
1,269. Robert Leslie Cooke
1,270. 749
1,271. O's lost 6–5 on penalties.
1,272. Michael George Conroy
1,273. David Jones-Quartey
1,274. O's lost at Mansfield Town.
1,275. Melvyn John Rees (sadly Rees died from cancer on 30 May 1993).
1,276. Stoke City
1,277. Daniel Benstock
1,278. O's lost 0–2 to Swansea City.
1,279. Fulham
1,280. Colin West
1,281. Ian Bogie, Mark Dempsey, Gary Barnett and Shaun Brooks all converted with Ian Hendon missing his spot-kick.
1,282. Birmingham City, O's lost 2–4 on aggregate.
1,283. 34,832 spectators watched the two-legged Final.
1,284. Darren Edward Pitcher
1,285. Daniel Brown
1,286. 37,284
1,287. O's mascot, Theo the Wyvern.
1,288. Five FA Cup goals
1,289. Scott Arron Houghton, he turned his back as goalie Lance Key was clearing the ball, it hit Houghton on the backside and flew into the net for O's winner.
1,290. Kelechi-Kristantos (KK) Opara
1,291. Chad Andrew Mansley
1,292. Lee Goodwin with a header on 102 minutes.

1,293. O's won at Portsmouth 4–1 with goals from Dean Smith, Steve Watts, Wayne Gray and Iyseden Christie. In fact O's netted all five goals, Smith scored for Pompey with an own-goal to open the scoring.

1,294. He joined Alfreton Town in August 2012, which is his 16th club.

1,295. 35,851

1,296. Ezomo Iriekpen

1,297. Daniel Ian Hatcher

1,298. O's beat Queen's Park Rangers with goals from Jamal Campbell-Ryce, Gary Fletcher and Lee Thorpe.

1,299. Margate by 1–0

1,300. The game was played at Dover Athletics' ground.

1,301. O's won at Grantham Town 2–1, with goals from Wayne Purser and Gary Alexander.

1,302. Bristol Rovers

1,303. Glyn Garner

1,304. O's won at Fulham 2–1 with goals from Craig Easton and Joseph Richard Keith.

1,304A. Derek Henry Duncan on 63 minutes.

1,305. O's beat Queens Park Rangers 2–1 with goals from Jason Demetriou and Adam Boyd (penalty).

1,306. Efe Echanomi on 43 minutes, it was his first competitive goal after being two years off due to a broken leg.

1,307. Ryan Jarvis, Adam Chambers, J.J. Melligan and Adam Boyd (pen).

1,308. Bradley Gray

1,309. Bristol Rovers, after a 3–3 aet, O's lost 6–5 on penalties.

1,310. Jason Demetriou and Daniel Patrick Granville.

1,311. Dean Cox and Ryan Jarvis.

1,312. Matthew Spring

1,313. O's were losing 2–0 to non-League Droylsden but came back to win 8–2.

1,314. Chorley (pen) 77 mins, Tehoue 89 mins, Mpoku 93 mins, McGleish 97 mins, Tehoue 99 mins, Tehoue 107 mins, McGleish 108 mins and McGleish 119 mins.

1,315.   Jimmy Smith

1,316.   Swansea City

1,317.   Jimmy Smith and an own-goal in the 88th minute by
         Alan Tait.

1,318.   Jonathan Téhoué

1,319.   59,361

1,319A. 8,923

1,320.   Michael Richardson

1,321.   Jamie Cureton

1,322.   Daniels, Cox, Chorley, Mooney, McSweeney, Laird, Forbes,
         Smith, Butcher, Porter, Odubajo, Daniels and Cox. It was
         Chorley who missed O's 14th spot-kick to send O's out.

1,323.   Blackburn Rovers

1,324.   O's beat Bromley 3–0 with goals from Matthew Spring,
         George Porter and Jimmy Smith.

1,325.   League Two side, Gillingham.

1,326.   Dennis Pacey with 12 FA Cup goals.

1,327.   Droylsden 8–2 in December 2010.

1,328.   274

1,329.   111

1,329A. P128 W36 D34 L58 F116 A210

1,330.   Yes, 404 scored and 396 conceded.